Preschool Prodigies

CHAPTER TWO

2

By: Robert and Samantha Young
Illustrations: Robert Young with art licensed at FreePik.com

Published by: Young Music, LLC
ISBN: 978-0999210109

2358 Dutch Neck Road
Smyrna, DE 19977

Prodigies Playground

THIS BOOK BELONGS TO:

Dear families & teachers,

Welcome back to the Preschool Prodigies Workbooks! It's time for more musical fun with Chapter Two.

In Chapter Two, we'll focus more on the concepts of low and high by introducing the High c bell. We'll also talk about left and right, and we'll continue to develop our understanding of C (Do) as our homebase note. Don't forget that we want to facilitate meaningful and memorable play with the different musical pitches so that your learner can develop a better understanding of pitch.

Like Chapter One, it is very important that you provide your learner with consistent, positive & fun opportunities to practice music. Your kids will benefit from a comfortable and encouraging practicing enviornment, and you are the perfect person to facilitate that for them!

Don't forget that the Playground videos that guide you through the book should be watched before AND after completing the workbook activities. Each section should be approached by watching the video, playing the sheet music, then completing the activities, and then circling back to watch or practice the sheet music again. It's important play the sheet music and the videos multiple times to provide lots of meaningful play with the notes, while also working on the physical skills needed for mastery of the song.

You'll also want to have your bells out while working through the books, that way you can play the sheet music and even play along with the activities as you play through the book.

As always, if you have any questions about the books or video content, we'd love to hear from you at Support@PreschoolProdigies.com.

Happy Musicing!

– Mr. Rob & The Prodigies Team

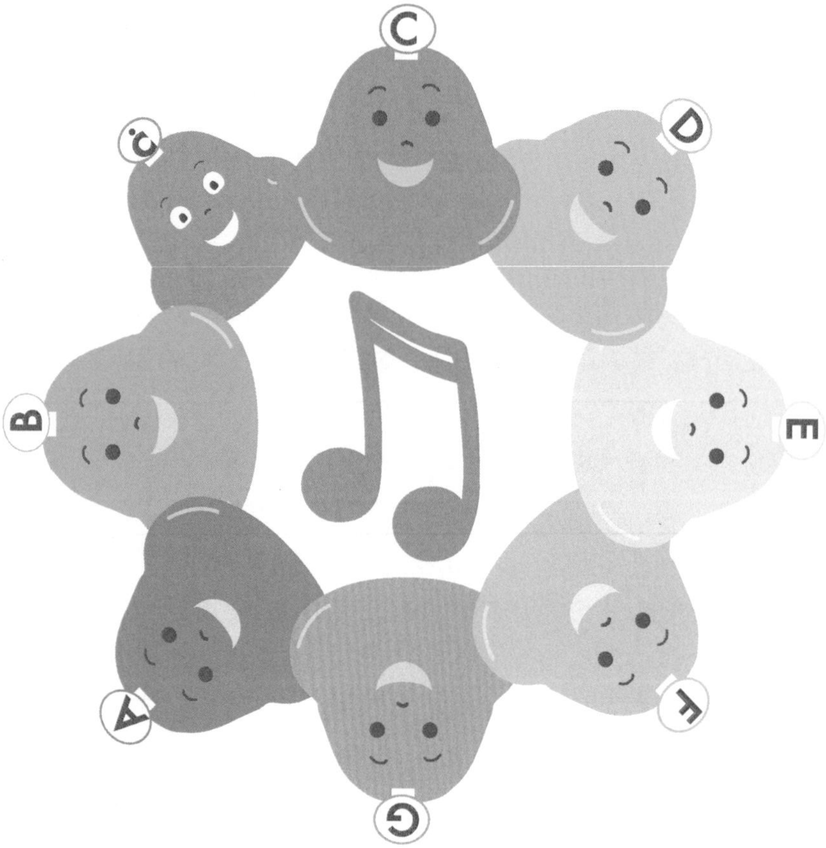
C
D
E
F
G
A
B
C

Chapter 2 Section 1: Low C & High C Lesson Guide

Objective

By the end of this section, students should be able to distinguish between high and low C.

Overview

In this section, students will distinguish between high and low sounds in both music and our daily enviornments.

Essential Question

How can a student distinguish between high and low sounds?

Instruction Tips

Give students the opportunity to practice their high voice and their low voice. Have your learner sing a familiar song in a high or low voice, or have a conversation with another person in a very high or low voice.

Materials

- C Bell
- Red Crayon
- Low C, High C Video Access
- Workbook pages: 6-11
- Scissors
- Tape or Glue

Table of Contents

Complementary Activities

Have a discussion about high and low sounds in the learner's enviornment.

Practice call & response with one person leading & the other following on high & low C.

Section 2.1 Video Annotations

0:50 Don't have an instrument? Pause here to practice the Low C hand-sign by making a fist near your waist.

0:55 Pause here and practice the hand sign for High C by making a fist near your head.

2:56 Pause and let your learner play both bells at one time. Resume when they're ready to play along with the video this way.

At the end ask "how can we distinguish the low C from the high c?"

Low C, High c

Lesson 2.1

☆☆☆☆☆

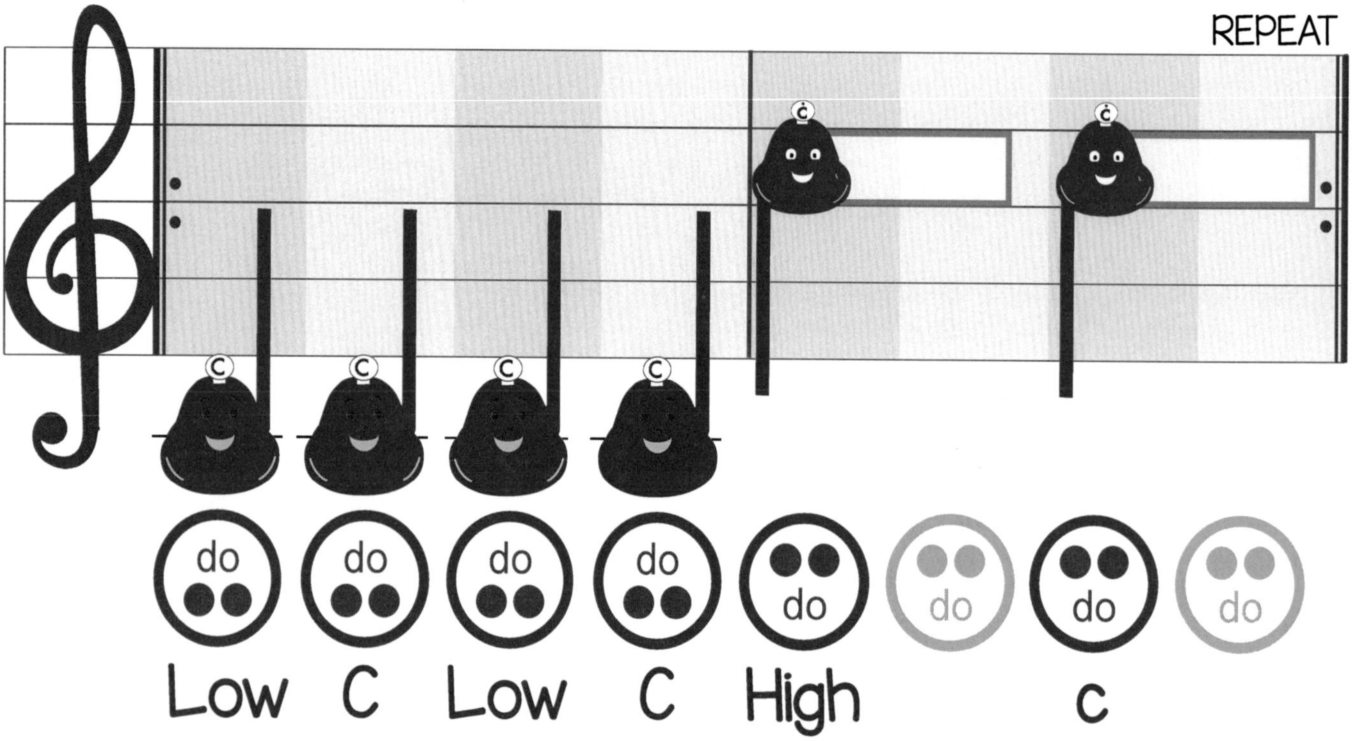

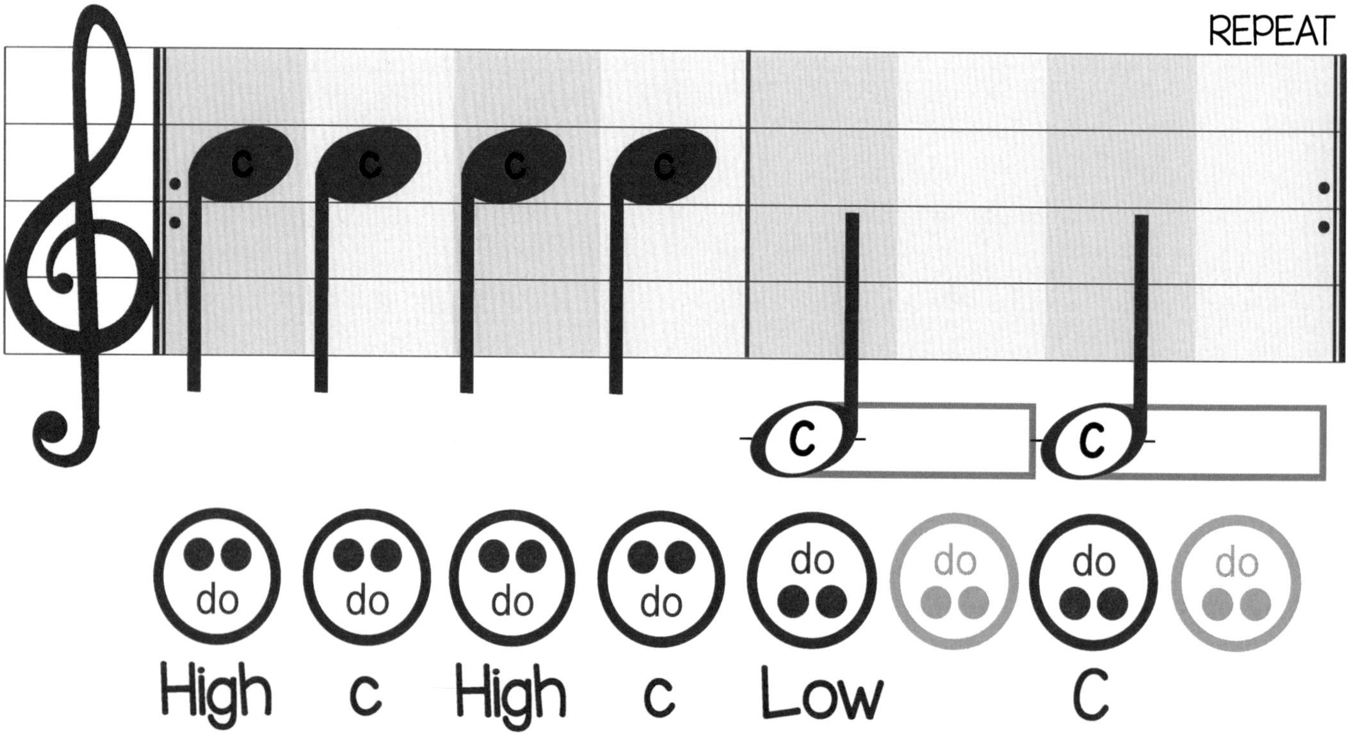

In this song, we're practicing with 2 red bells, Low C and High c.
Don't forget to **sing and play at the same time!** This helps build your musical ear. Also, don't forget to play each line TWO TIMES before moving onto the next line! That's why we have the repeat sign 𝄆 𝄇

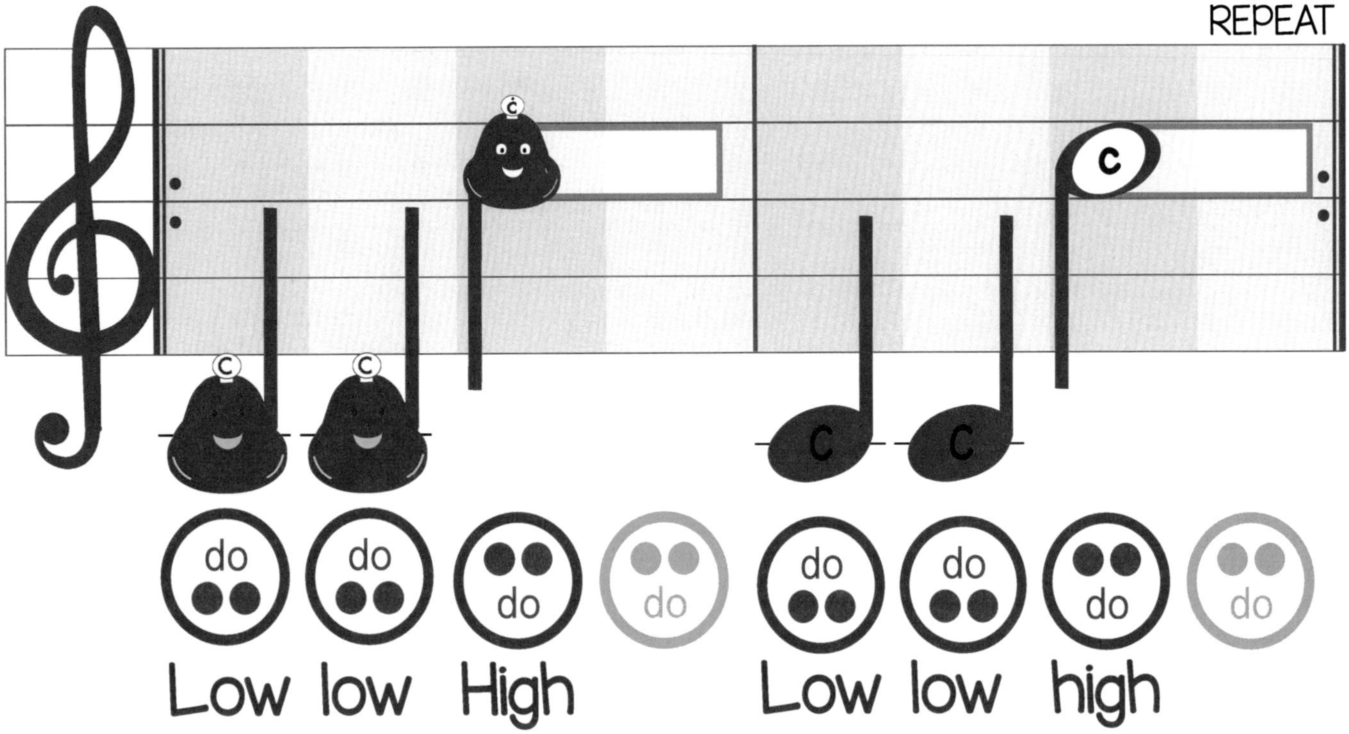

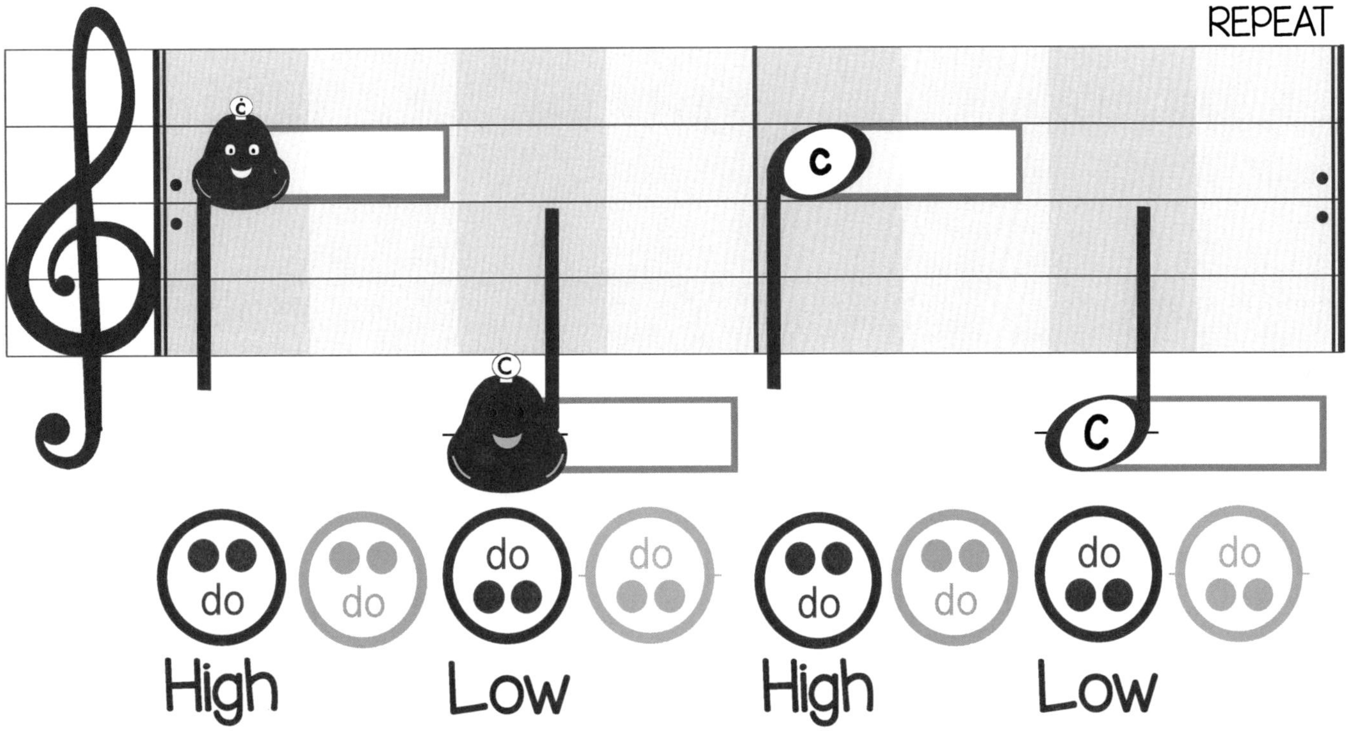

High or Low?

Trace each name of each image below. Does it make a high sound or a low sound? Circle the answer!

lion

high or low

dolphin

high or low

dino

high or low

squirrel

high or low

bird

high or low

dog

high or low

truck

high or low

teapot

high or low

bear

high or low

High or Low?

Trace each name of each image below. Does it make a high sound or a low sound? Circle the answer!

boat

high or low

horn

high or low

whistle

high or low

drum

high or low

triangle

high or low

cat

high or low

grandma

high or low

cow

high or low

pirate

high or low

Red

Finish the Pattern

A PATTERN is anything that repeats! There are patterns in music, in the weather, in the seasons, in the days of the week and all around us!

Can you complete the patterns below?
Cirlce the BIG C for low C, and the tiny c for high c.

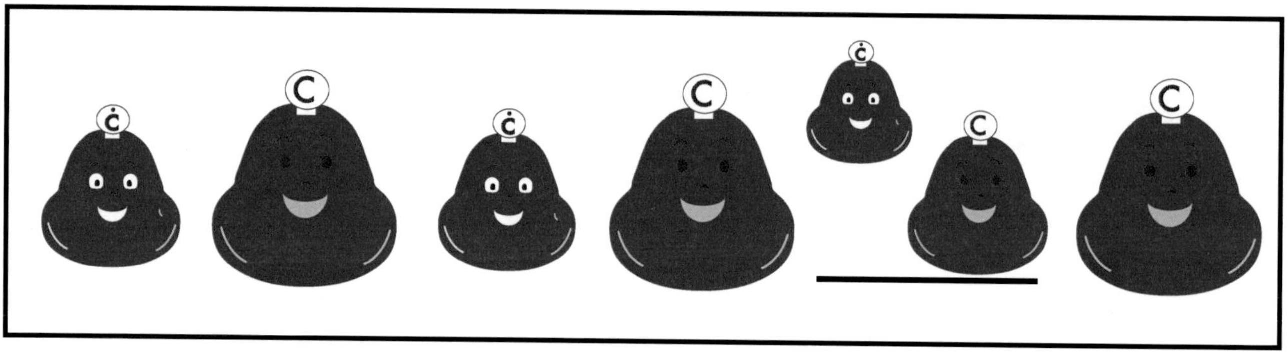

Write a Song

Trace the sound each bell makes, then cut out each square. Next, paste the squares in the boxes to make a song. Play your song with high and low C once it's pasted.

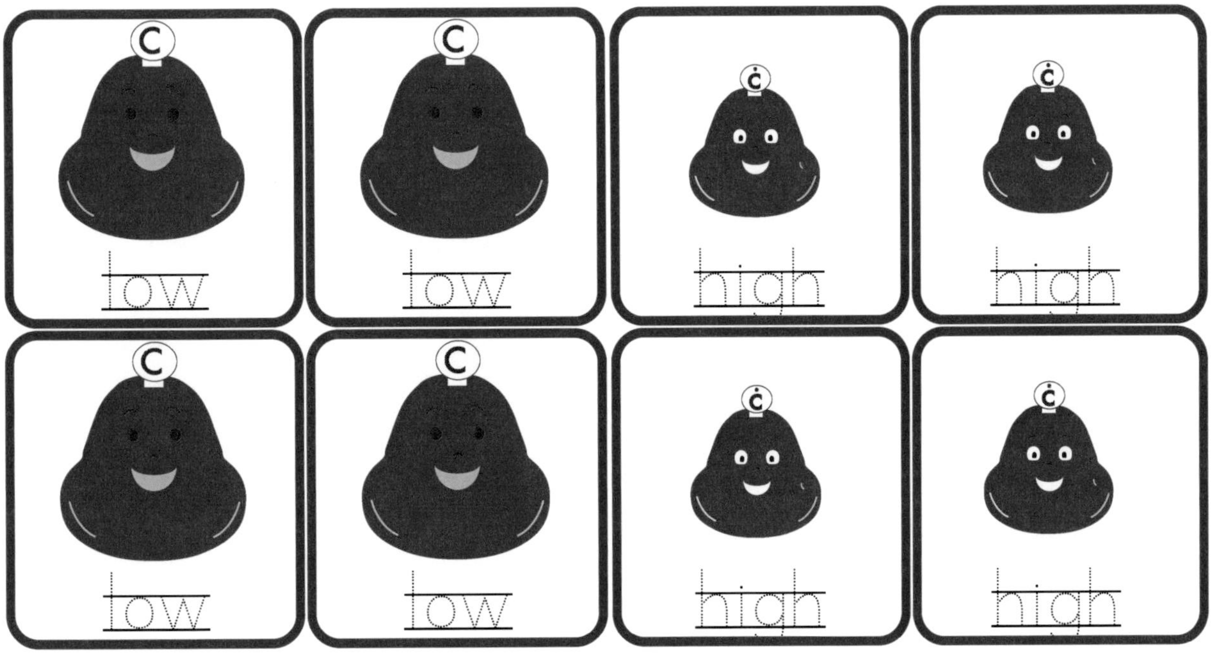

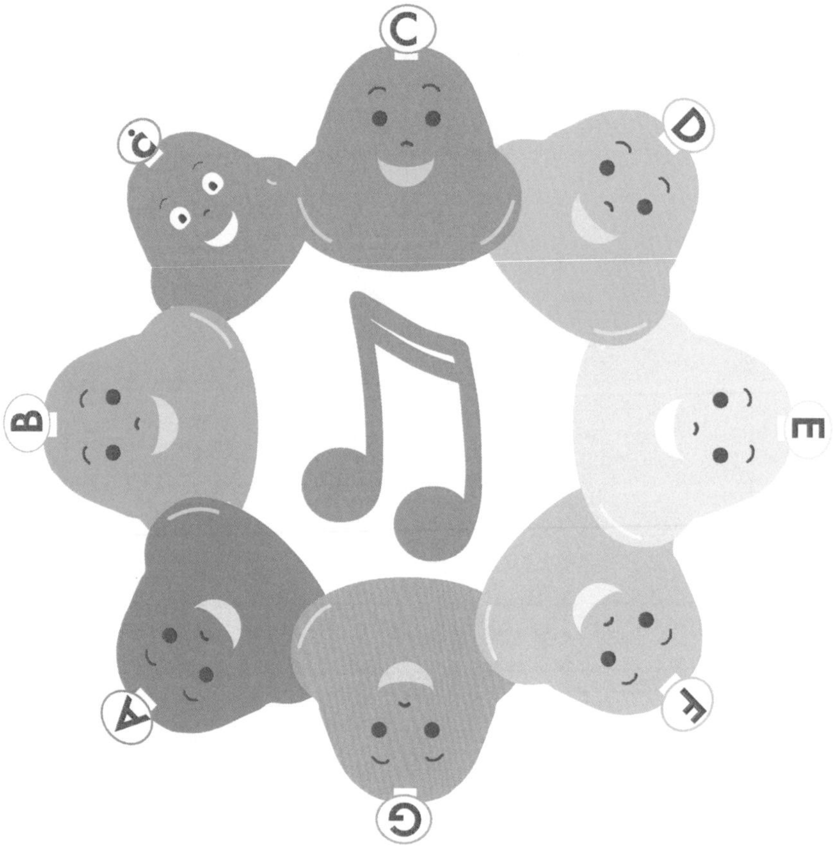
C
D
E
F
G
A
B
C

Chapter 2 Section 2: Left & Right C Lesson Guide

Objective

By the end of this section, students should be able to identify the C / 1 bell on the left and the c / 8 bell on the right.

Overview

In this section, students will learn about left and right by playing the Low C / 1 bell with the left hand, and the High c / 8 bell with the right hand.

Essential Question

How can a student distinguish between left and right?

Instruction Tips

Each student will learn this skill at his or her own pace. Distinguishing left from right can take some children longer to grasp. Keep reinforcing their knowledge of left and right and don't worry if it takes some learners a little longer.

Materials

- C Bell
- Red Crayon
- Left C, Right C Video Access
- Workbook pages: 14-19

Table of Contents

Complementary Activities

Play a call and response pattern using the low C and high c. Allow your learner to play a series of notes, and then play them back for them. Switch roles.

Section 2.2 Video Annotations

1:00 Pause and make sure that students understand they should be playing their bell when the animated bell hits the red box on the screen (past the pipe).

1:15 If students miss the quick rhythm change here, go back to 1:04 and try again.

2:40 Make sure students are playing two notes on each side; practice a few times before resuming the video.

Red

Left C & Right c

Lesson 2.2

☆☆☆☆☆

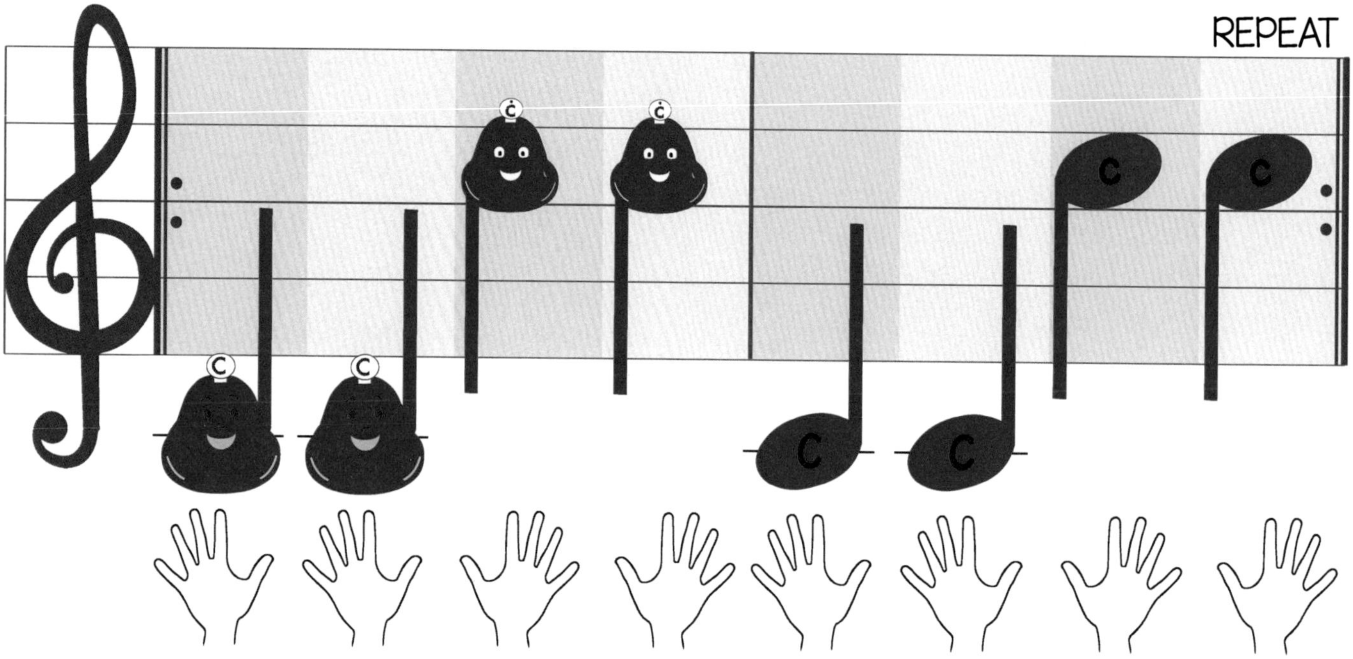

Left left Right right Left left Right right

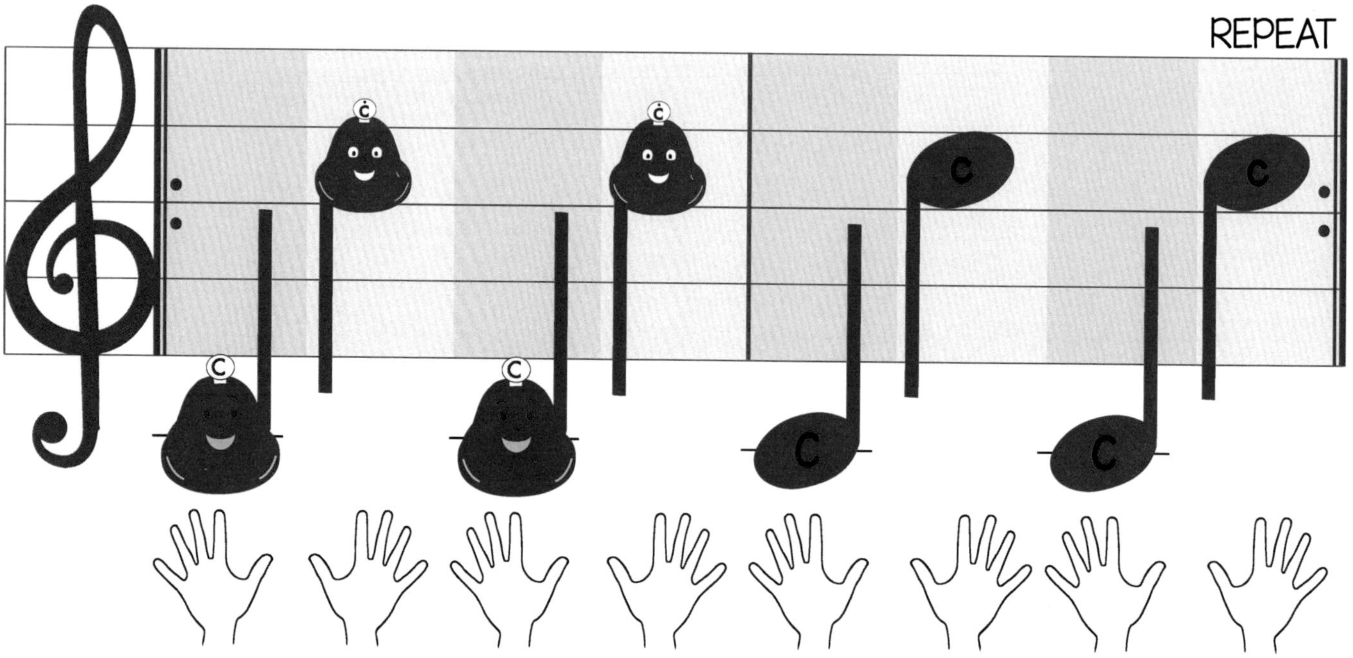

Left Right Left Right Left Right Left Right

Red

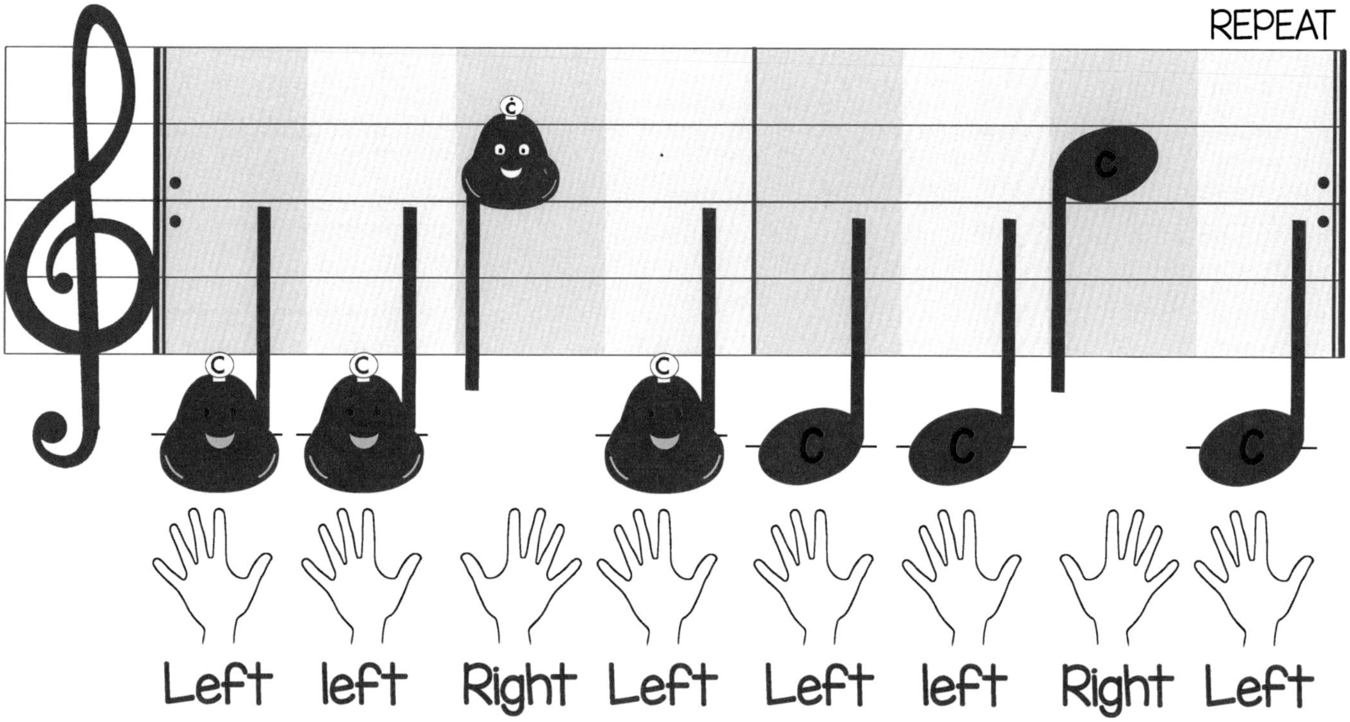
REPEAT
Left left Right Left Left left Right Left

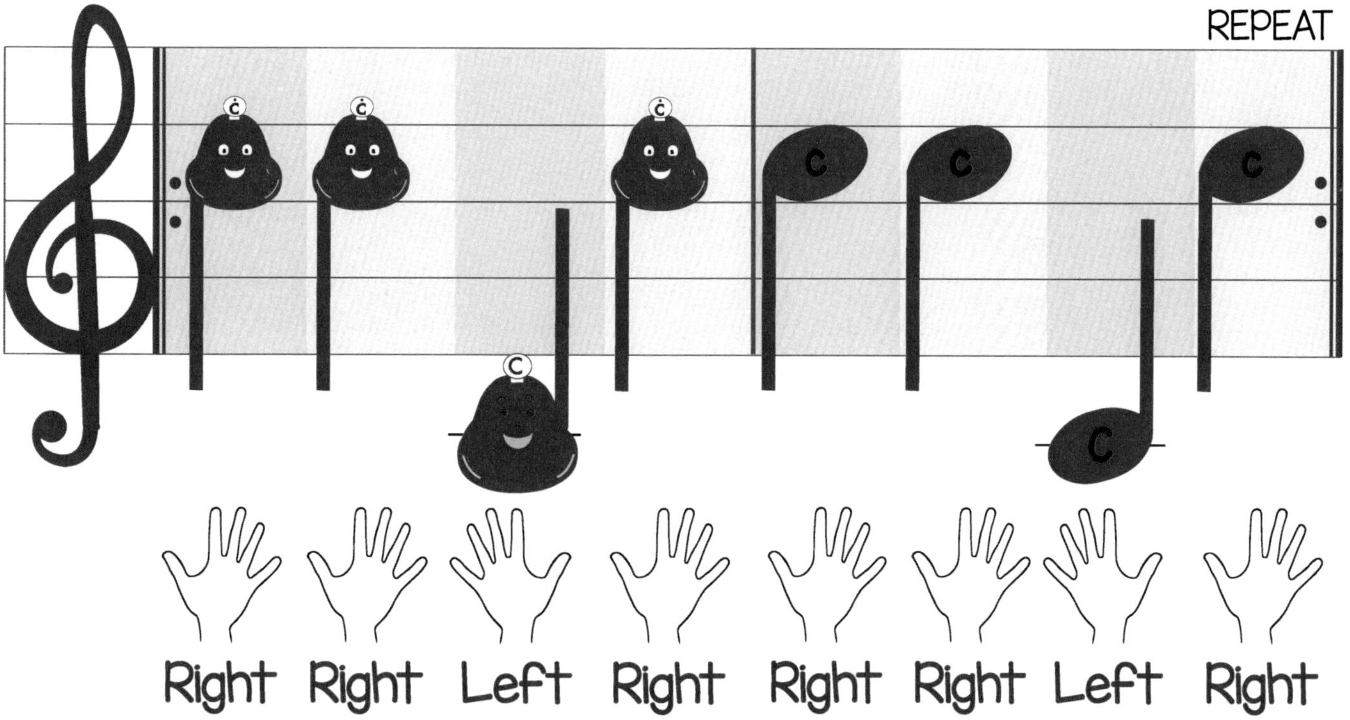
REPEAT
Right Right Left Right Right Right Left Right

Red

Left & Right

Trace the words "Left" and "Right". Draw a BIG C on the left hand. Draw a little c bell on the right hand. If you can, write an L or the word left on the left hand.If you can, right an R or the word right on the right hand.

left
left
left

right
right
right

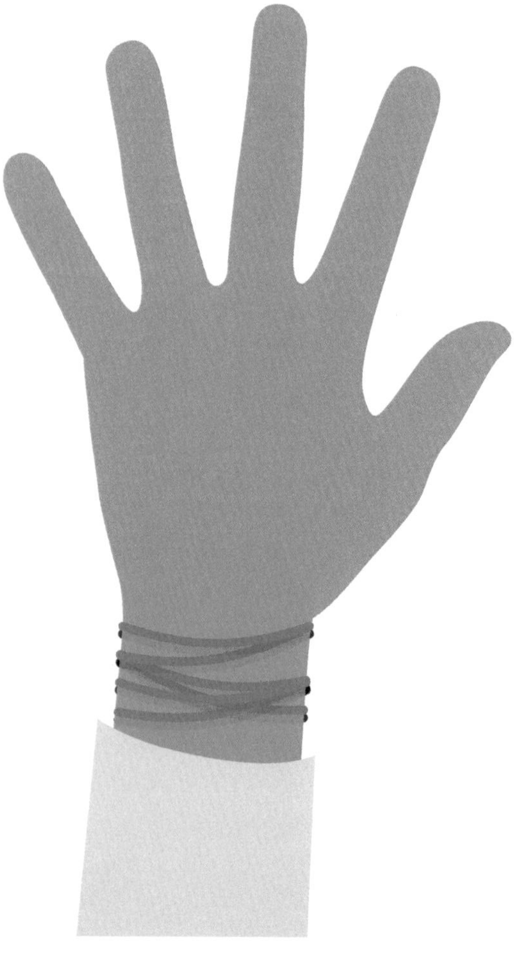

Left or Right?

Trace the words "left" and right", then follow the directions in each box to circle one of each pair.

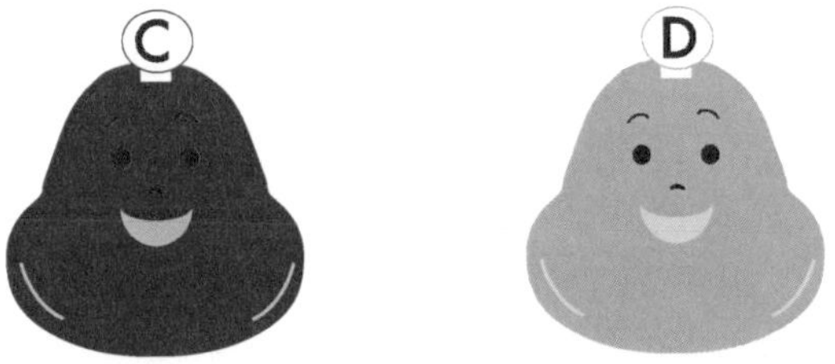

Circle the bell on the left.

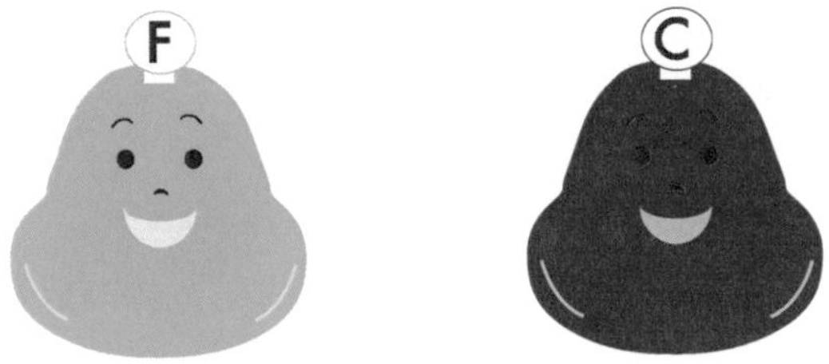

Circle the bell on the right.

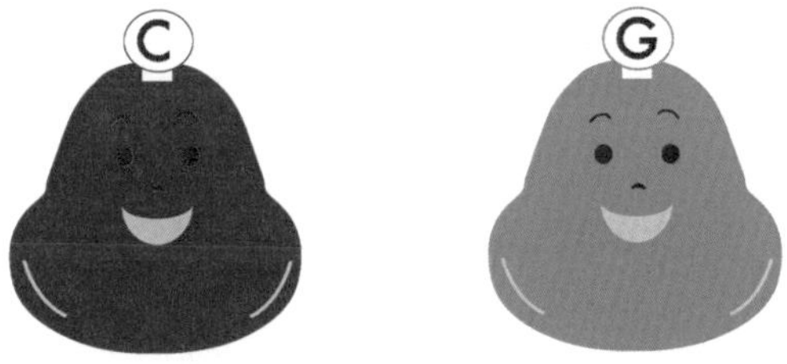

Circle the bell on the left.

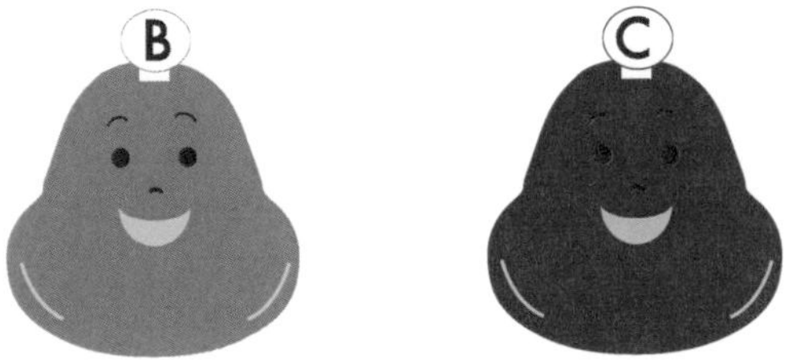

Circle the bell on the right.

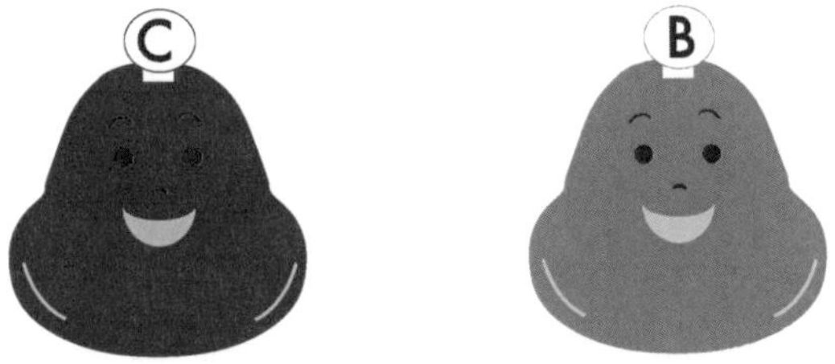

Circle the bell on the left.

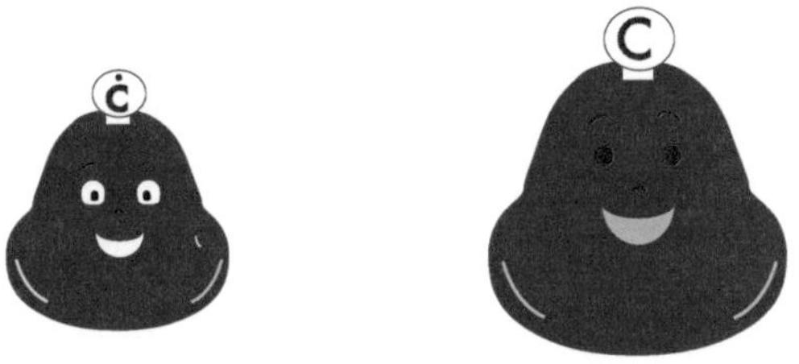

Circle the bell on the right.

Circle the bell on the left.

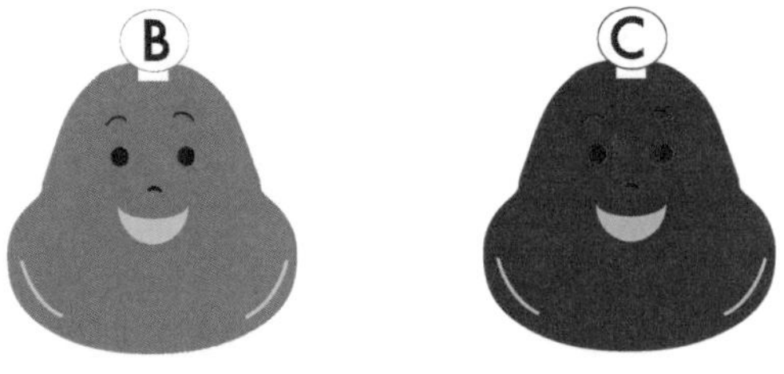

Circle the bell on the right.

Direction

Some bells are looking left, others are looking right!

Circle the bells that are looking **left**!

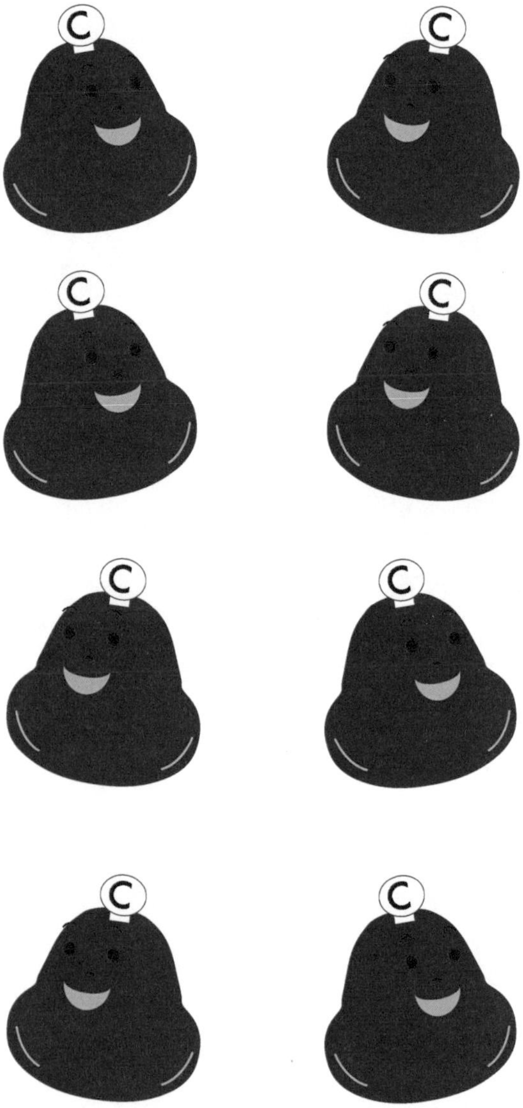

Trace each word below:

left left

left left

Circle the bells that are looking **right**!

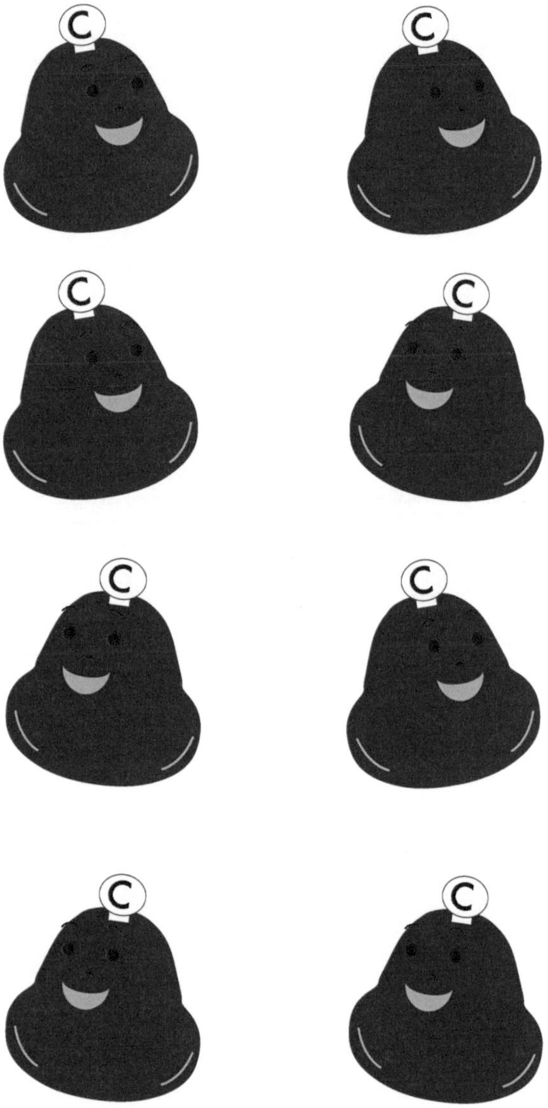

Trace each word below:

right right

right right

Red

Maze

Let the C bell guide you through the maze below!

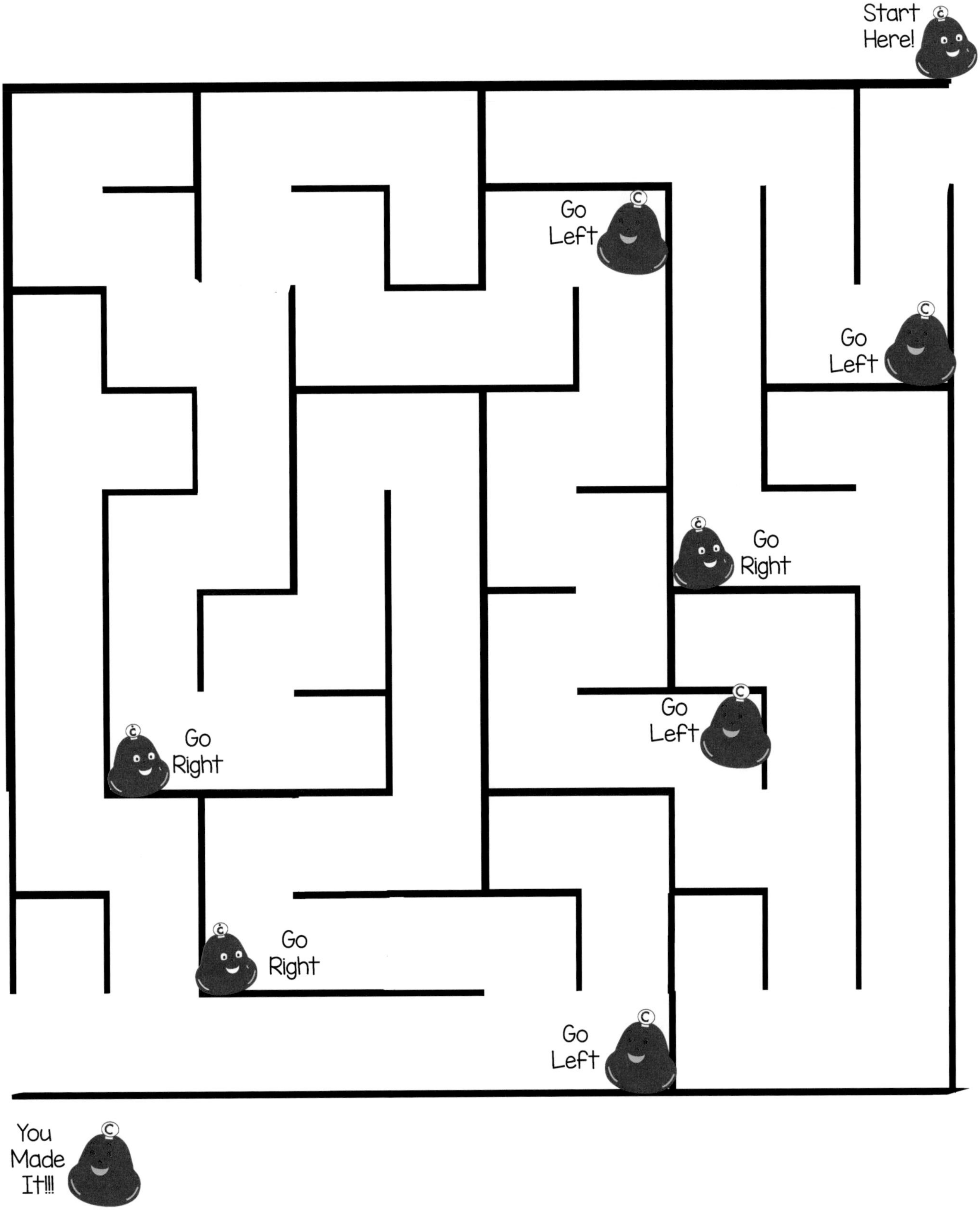

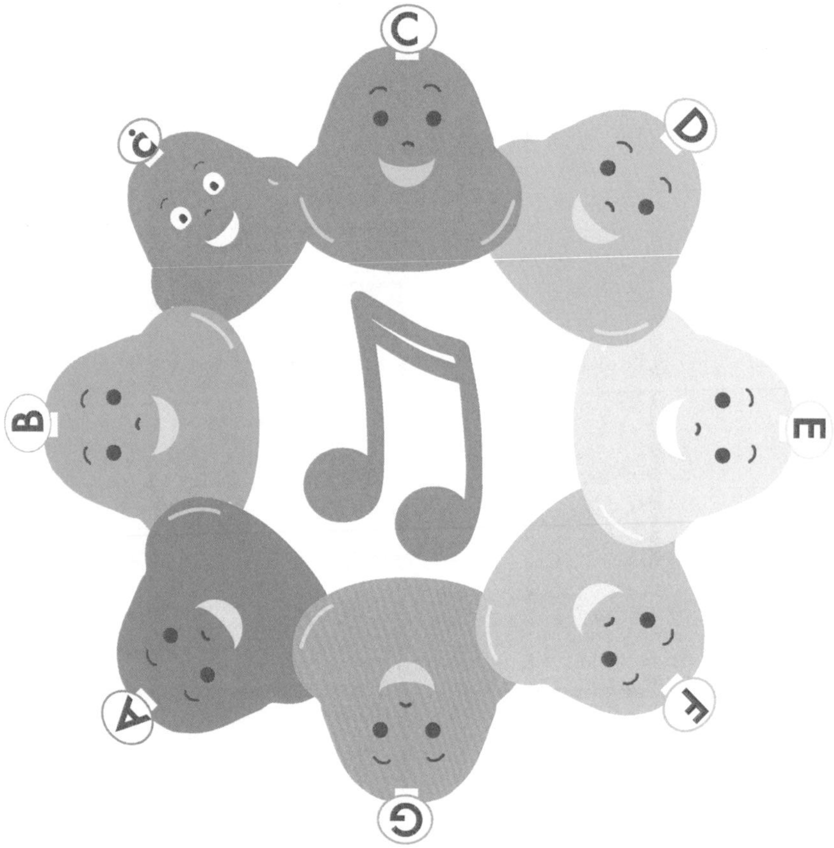
C
D
E
F
G
A
B
C

Chapter 2 Section 3: Low C v High c Lesson Guide

Objective

By the end of this section, students should be able to differentiate between the low C and the high c.

Overview

In this section, students will play a listening game in which they differentiate between the low and high c.

Essential Question

How can a student distinguish between low and high c?

Instruction Tips

In this section there will be many opportunities for students to test their listening skills. Do what works best for the class--try the listening game as a whole class, with partners or in small groups. See what works best for your learners.

Materials

- Low C Bell • High c Bell
- Red Crayon
- Low C v High c Video Access
- Workbook pages: 22-27
- Scissors
- Tape or Glue

Table of Contents

Complementary Activities

Play a call and response pattern using the low C and high c. Allow your learner to play a series of notes, and then play them back for them. Switch roles.

Section 2.3 Video Annotations

1:09 Pause and ask students which bell they think it is. Let students shout their guess or hold up their lion and bird cards from this section's workbook activities.

1:47 Pause and ask your learners to visualize the sound of each bell throughout the video. Ask them to notice if any pictures come to mind or if there is any way that they distinguish one bell from the other as they continue listening.

Pause any time the students are not listening carefully. Explain to them that we have to listen very carefully in order to correctly identify each note.

Red

Low C or High c?

Lesson 2.3

☆☆☆☆☆

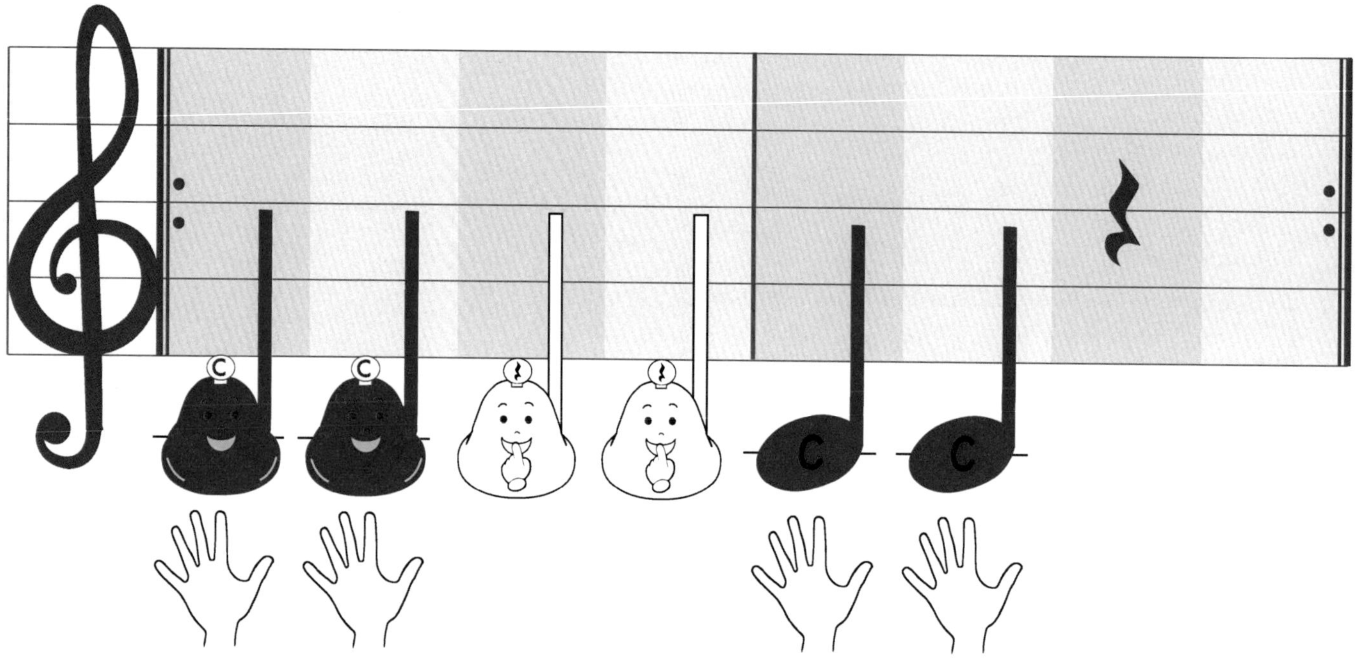

Low **Left** Shh Shh **Low** **Left** Rest Rest

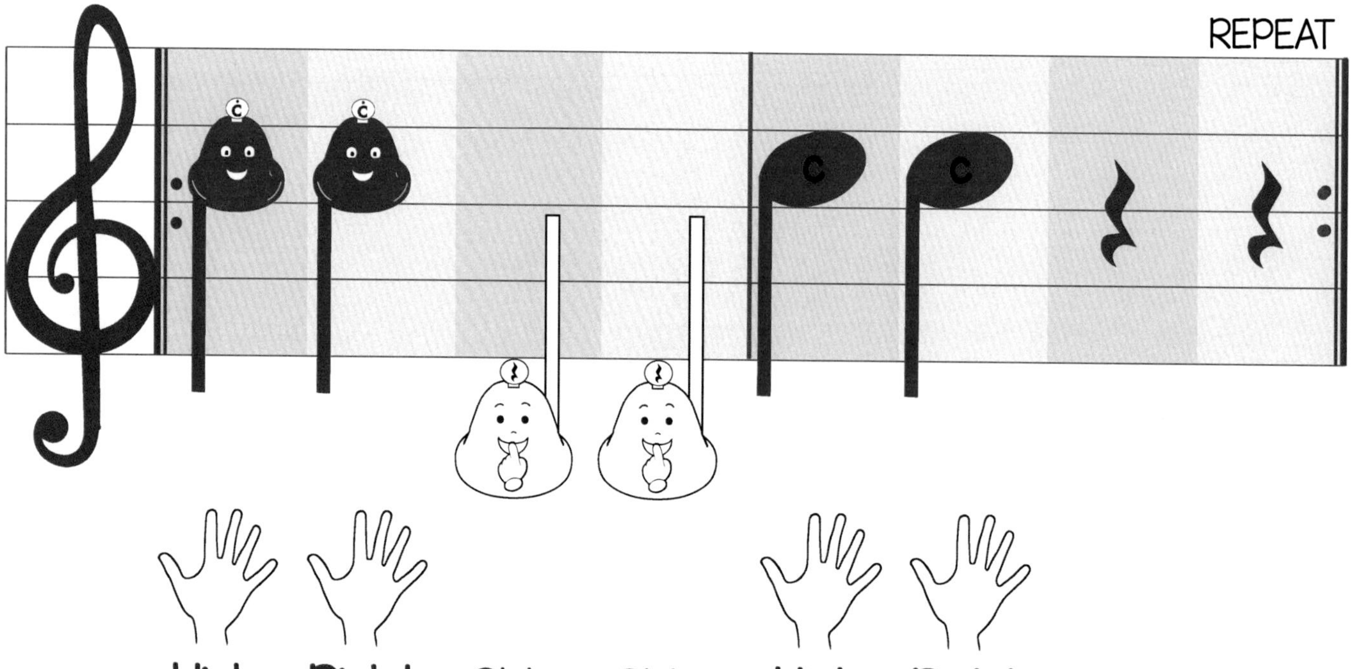

High **Right** Shh Shh **High** **Right** Rest Rest

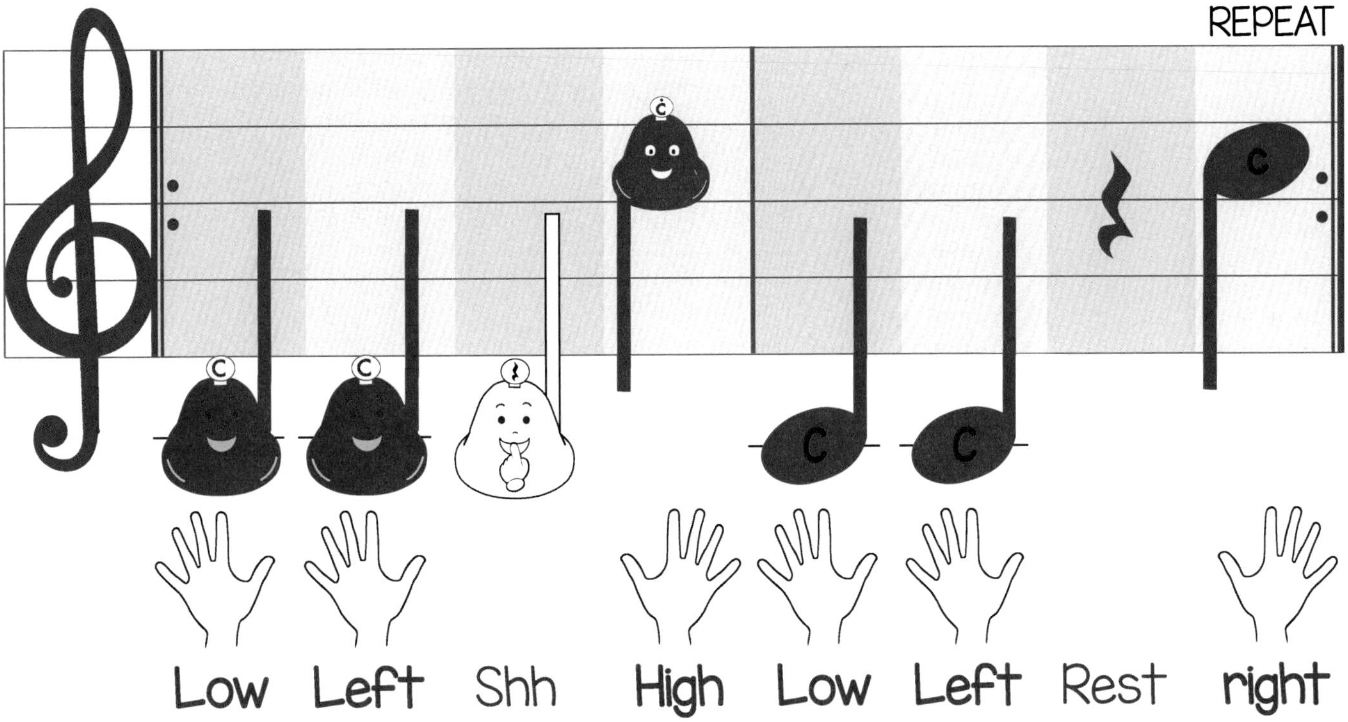
REPEAT
C
C
C
C
C
C
Low
Left
Shh
High
Low
Left
Rest
right

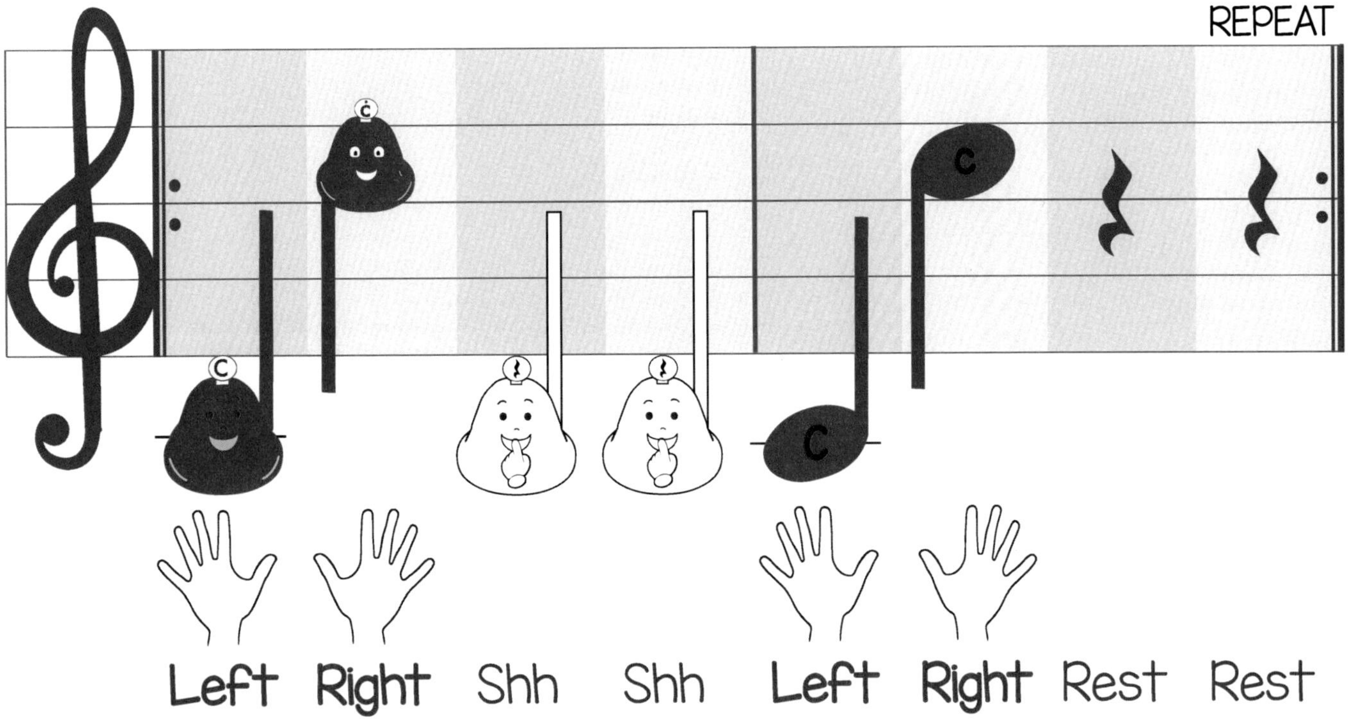
REPEAT
C
C
C
C
Left
Right
Shh
Shh
Left
Right
Rest
Rest

Patterns with Left & Right

Let's try some more patterns with Left (Low C) and Right (High c).
The patterns start out okay, but then we have some blank spaces!
Fill in the missing blocks with L or R to complete the pattern!
Then try playing the patterns on your bells.

L	L	R	R	L		R	R
L	R	L	R	L			R
L	L	L	R	L		L	
R	L	L	L	R		L	L
L	L	R	L	L	L		L
R	L	R	R	R		R	R

Lions and Birds

Let's play a listening game. You will need two people!
Player 1 has both red bells. Player 2 closes her eyes.
Player 1 plays 1 of the red bells, and then waits.
Player 2 listens, and tries to guess which bell they heard!
If you hear a low sound, circle the lion.
If you hear a high sound, circle the bird.
Play 8 rounds, then switch!

1 

2 

3 

4 

5 

6 

7 

8 

Matching

Match Low C to the low sounds and match High c to the high sounds!

Listening Game Cards

Cut out the rectangles below. Then fold along the middle line and tape/glue a popsicle stick on the inside.
Now you can continue to play listening games like we did in the video and in Lions and Birds. Use your cards to answer and see who has the fastest ears!

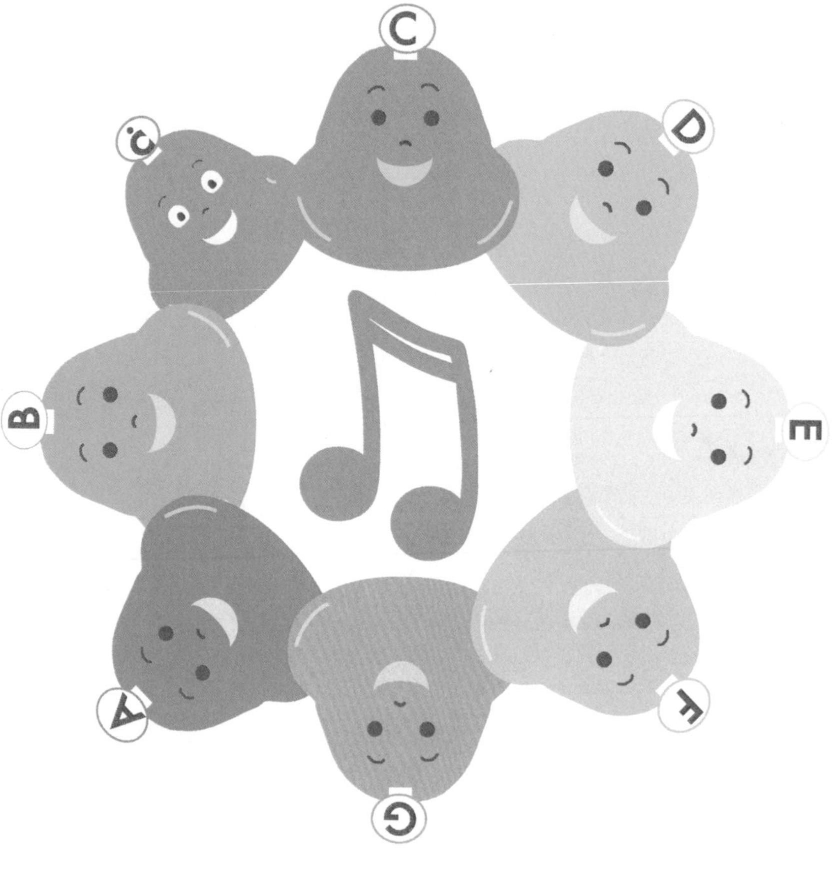
C
D
E
F
G
A
B
C

Chapter 2 Section R: Beet & Cherry Lesson Guide

Objective

By the end of this section, students should be able to clap, tap or stomp both a quarter note and an eighth note rhythm.

Overview

In this section, students will add eighth notes to their rhythm practice. Students will learn about eighth notes and quarter notes, also known as "cherry" and "beet".

Essential Question

How are the eighth note and quarter note different?

Instruction Tips

Students will likely requst this song again and again. Take advantage of their enthusiasm by letting them clap and sing along with it has many times as you can allow.

Materials

- Red Crayon
- Beet & Cherry Video Access
- Workbook pages: 30-36

Table of Contents

Complementary Activities

Play a call and response pattern using the cherry and beet. Pause the video and allow students to make up their own call & response rhythm sections for Sweet Beets.

Section 2.R Video Annotations

0:47 Pausing here is a great opportunity to remind your learner that 'beet' is ONE syllable, and 'CHER-RY' is TWO syllables and that's why we use these words to represent our beats.
1:36 This is the beginning of the call and response section. Mr. Rob 'calls' it out, then your learner responds.

Explain to the students that Sweet Beets is a pun. A pun is a joke based on a word that can have more than one meaning. A beet is a delicious root vegetable; a beat is a unit of musical measurement.

Beet & Cherry

Lesson 2.R

☆☆☆☆☆

Sing the chorus to Sweet Beets while tapping a steady beat. Then in the verses, tap, clap or stomp with Beet and Cherry.

CHORUS 1

Sweet Beets, we've got some!
If you want some Sweet Beets, we've got 'em.
If you want Sweet Beets, we've got some,
If you want some Sweet Beets, we've got 'em.

VERSE 1

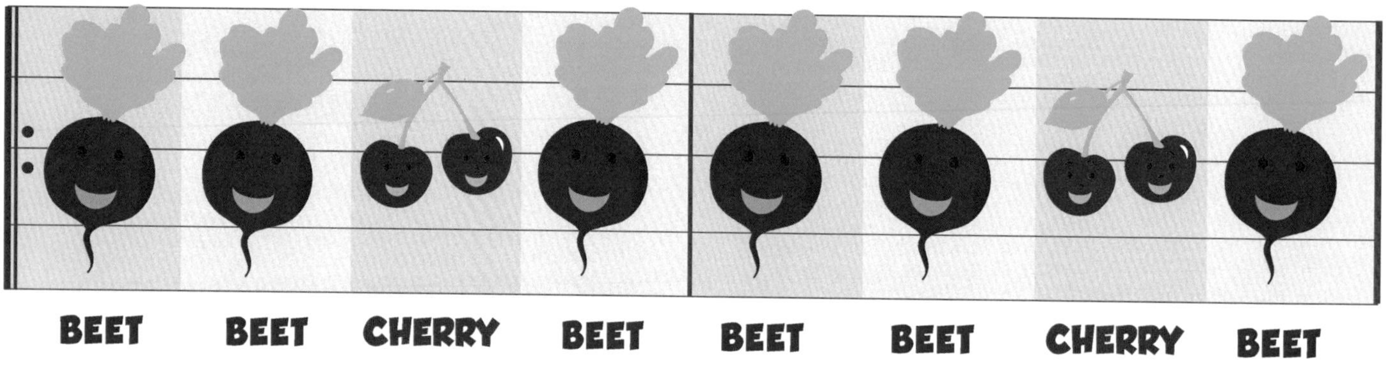

CHORUS 2

Sweet Beets, we've got some!
If you want some Sweet Beets, we've got 'em.
If you want Sweet Beets, we've got some,
If you want some Sweet Beets, we've got 'em.

VERSE 2

CHORUS 3

Sweet Beets, we've got some!
If you want some Sweet Beets, we've got 'em.
If you want Sweet Beets, we've got some,
If you want some Sweet Beets, we've got 'em.

VERSE 3

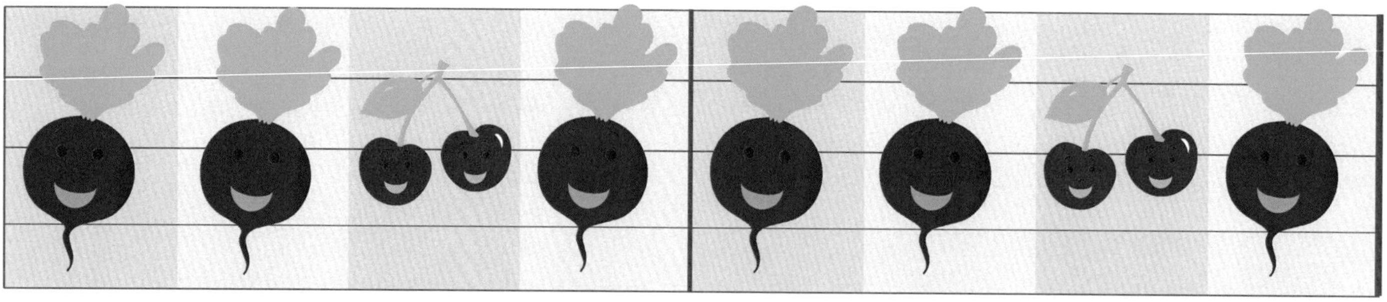

BEET BEET CHERRY BEET BEET BEET CHERRY BEET

CHERRY CHERRY BEET BEET CHERRY CHERRY BEET BEET

CHERRY BEET CHERRY BEET CHERRY BEET CHERRY BEET

CHERRY CHERRY CHERRY BEET CHERRY CHERRY CHERRY BEET

CHORUS 4

Sweet Beets, we've got some!

If you want some Sweet Beets, we've got 'em.

If you want Sweet Beets, we've got some,

If you want some Sweet Beets, we've got 'em.

Tas & Ti-Tis

You can also play rhythms with short syllables like Ta and Ti-Ti. Try singing, tapping, clapping or stomping your way through the rhythms below.

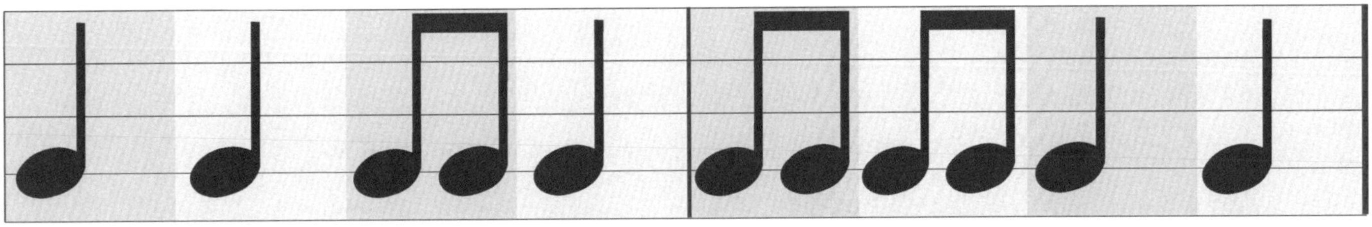

TA TA TI TI TA TI TI TI TI TA TA

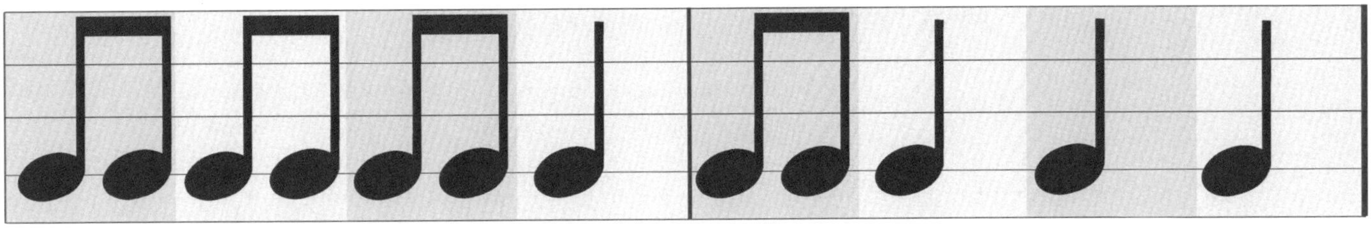

TI TI TI TI TI TI TA TI TI TA TA TA

TA TI TI TI TI TA TI TI TA TI TI TA

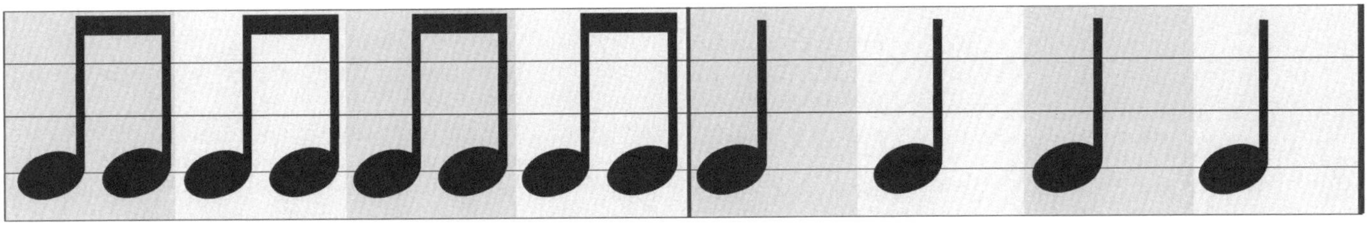

TI TI TI TI TI TI TI TI TA TA TA TA

Eighth Notes

Did you notice that the Cherry (Ti Ti) only take up one space in the measure? Even though they make two sounds, they still only take up the space of one Beet (Ta). That's because they are eighth notes.

Eighth notes are a faster type of note. It takes 2 eighth notes to fill one beat and 8 eighth notes to fill one full measure. You may have noticed when we were singing Sweet Beets that we sang and clapped "cherry" faster than "beet".

Practice drawing eighth notes below.

How Many Beats?

Each gray box represents one musical space (beat) in the measure. Most of the measures we'll see have four beats in them, but sometimes there are more or less. Count the number of beats in each measure below and write the number in each space to the right.

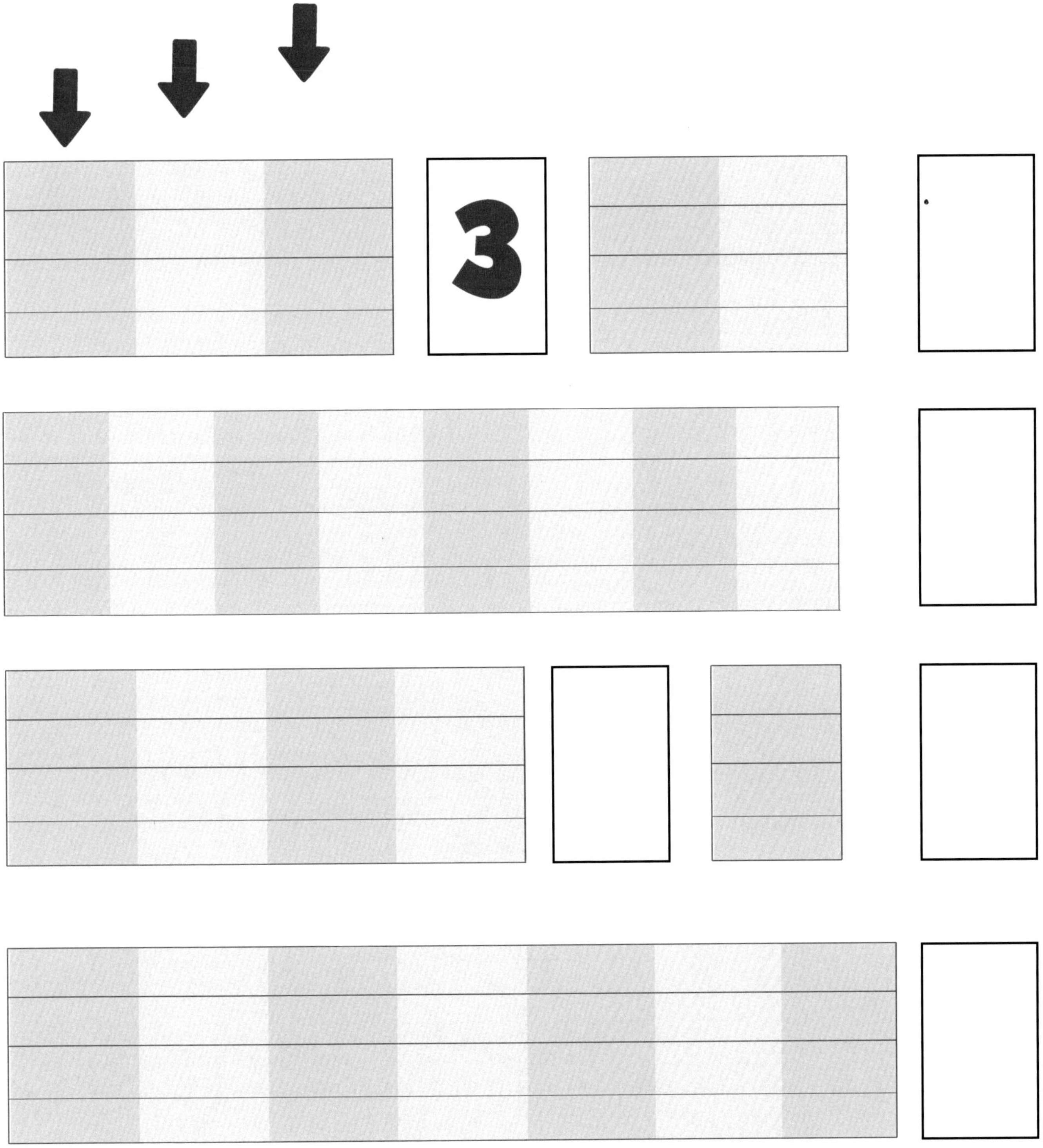

Write Your Own Rhythm

On the staffs below, write your own rhythm practice using either quarter notes & eighth notes or beets & cherries. Clap, stomp, beat or snap your rhythm once you've recorded it below.

Chapter 2 Section 4: C Sock Slide Lesson Guide

Objective

By the end of this section, students should be able to distinguish left from right.

Overview

In this section, students continue to practice with left and right.

Essential Question

How can a student differentiate left from right?

Instruction Tips

This lesson is fun for students because Mr. Rob encourages them to play the bells with their feet! Let them have fun and embrace the silliness of the exercise. This will add to their stores of positive memories assoicated with music.

Materials

- Low C Bell • High c Bell
- Red Crayon
- C Sock Slide Video Access
- Workbook pages: 38-43
- Scissors
- Tape or Glue

Table of Contents

Complementary Activities

Use the C chord cube to play a vocabulary game. Toss the cube and catch it. Which ever panel your right thumb lands on, your learner has to tell you why that element is related to C.

Section 2.4 Video Annotations

0:36 Pause here and explain that it's actually harder to play the bells with our feet. Give them a few opportunities to practice tapping each bell with their foot before resuming.

1:50 Pause here and ask your learner when they should be playing each bell. If they're not sure, play the video for a few seconds asking them to observe when the bell is played. They should notice that the bell is played when the fire comes out of the bottom.

Bell Stomp

Lesson 2.4

Trace the capital letters L and R, and then play this song with your feet!

L = 

R = 

L L L L

R R R R

L L R R

R R L L

Red

The pattern of left and right on this page is a famous rhythm called the paradiddle.

Can you play and memorize the paradiddle?

L  R 

L R L L

R L R R

L R L L

R L R R

C Sorting

Draw an arrow from each bell to the side where it belongs, then trace each word below.

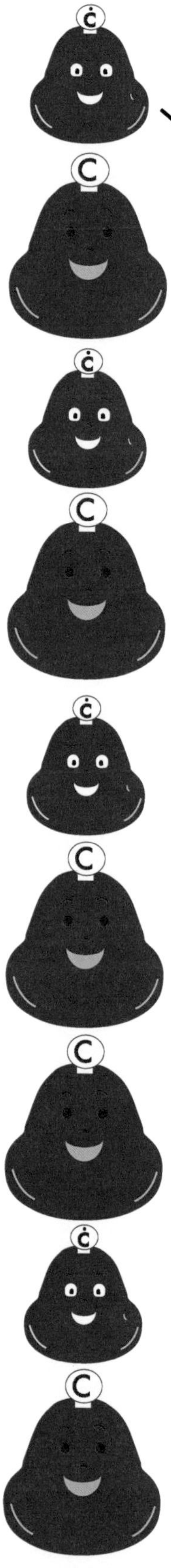

L R

left left right right

left left right right

left left right right

low high

low high

Red

Directions

Circle the bells that are looking in the same direction
as the first in each row.

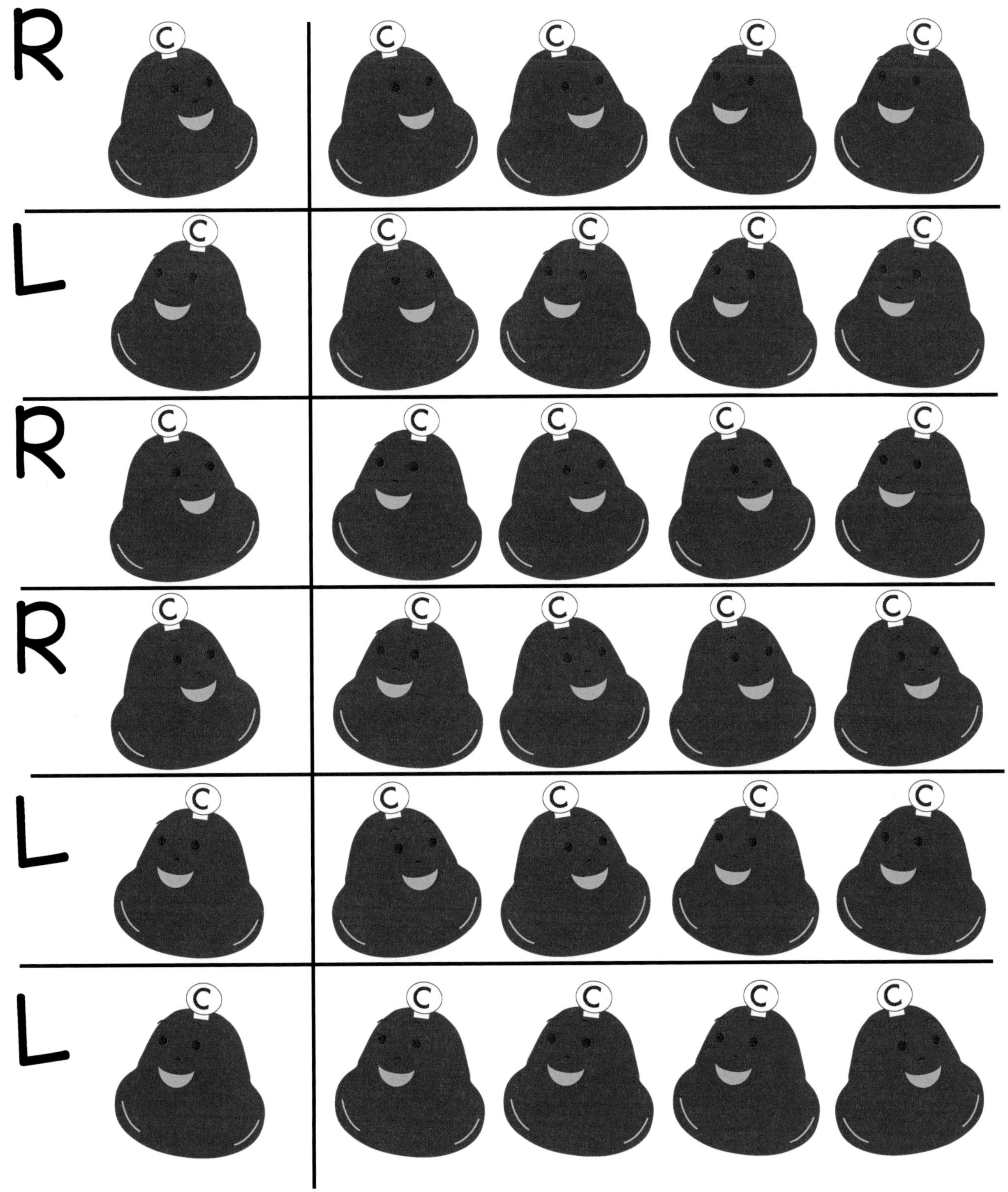

Which Way?

Color the left arrows **red** and circle the right arrows!

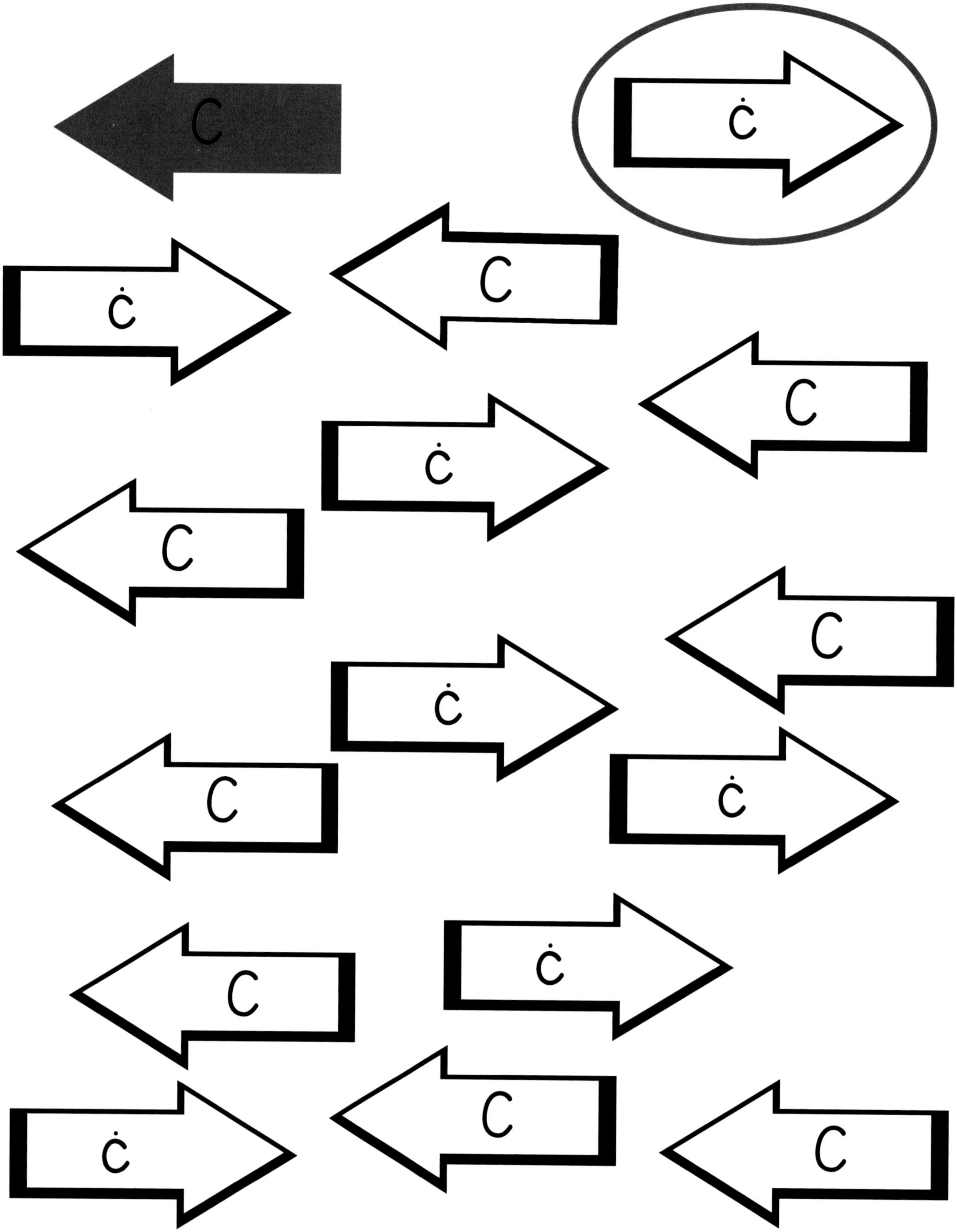

C Cube

Cut along the dotted line.
Fold the inside black lines.
Then tape your cube
along the edges.
Practice vocabulary with
your new cube and save it
for an activity later this
chapter!

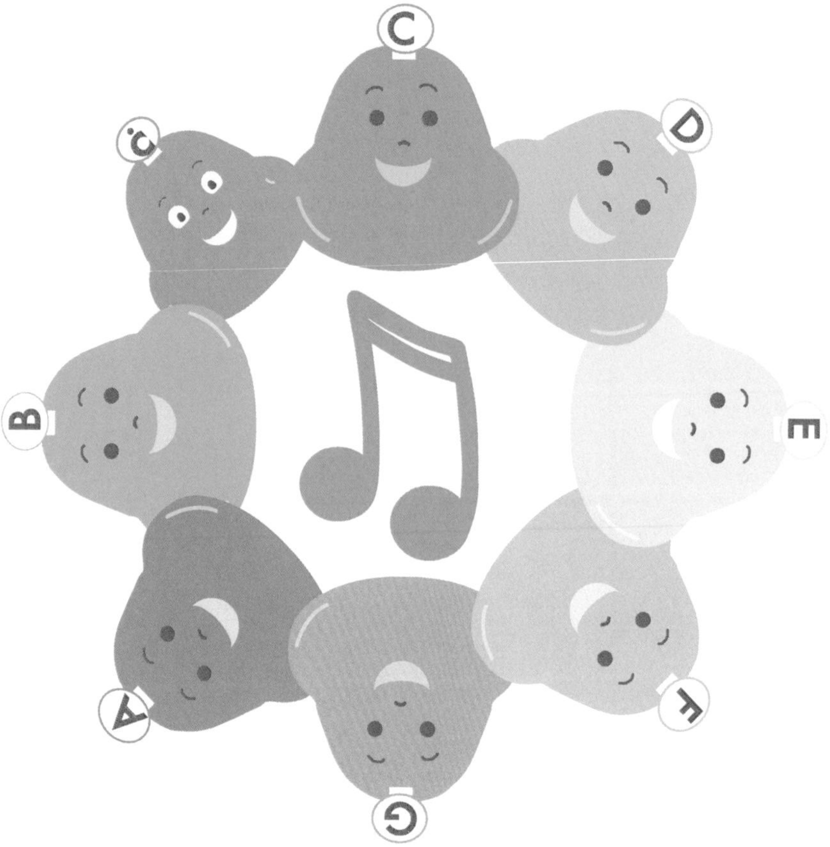
C
D
E
F
G
A
B
Ċ

Chapter 2 Section 5: C Chord Slide Lesson Guide

Objective

By the end of this section, students should be able to build a C Major chord and sing with Do, Mi, Sol and High Do.

Overview

This section reviews the C Major Chord we learned in Chapter 1. It also adds the High c bell to the chord and the challenge of playing two notes at the same time!

Essential Question

How can a student build a C Major chord?

Instruction Tips

If students are having trouble playing more than one bell at a time, have them experiment with the positioning of their bells.

Materials

- Low C Bell • E Bell • GBell
- High c Bell
- Red Crayon • Yellow Crayon
- C Chord Slide Video Access
- Workbook pages: 47-57
- Scissors
- Tape or Glue

Table of Contents

Complementary Activities

Use the E chord cube to play a vocabulary game. Toss the cube and catch it. Which ever panel your right thumb lands on, your learner has to tell you how that element represents E.

Section 2.5 Video Annotations

0:42 Pause here and ask students to practice playing two bells at the same time, then three and then all four. Tell them to try playing with their whole arms or moving the bells into a square position if they're having trouble playing all four bells at once.

0:55 Pause here and go back to 0:47 to give students a chance to start again now that they know the rhythm of the video.

1:25 If this pace is too fast for your learner, take advantage of the green playback speed buttons at the bottom of the screen. Slow down the pace if your learner seems frustrated.

C
D
E
F
G
A
B
C

Do Mi Sol do Bell Mat

Use this bell mat when practicing the 2.5 lesson.

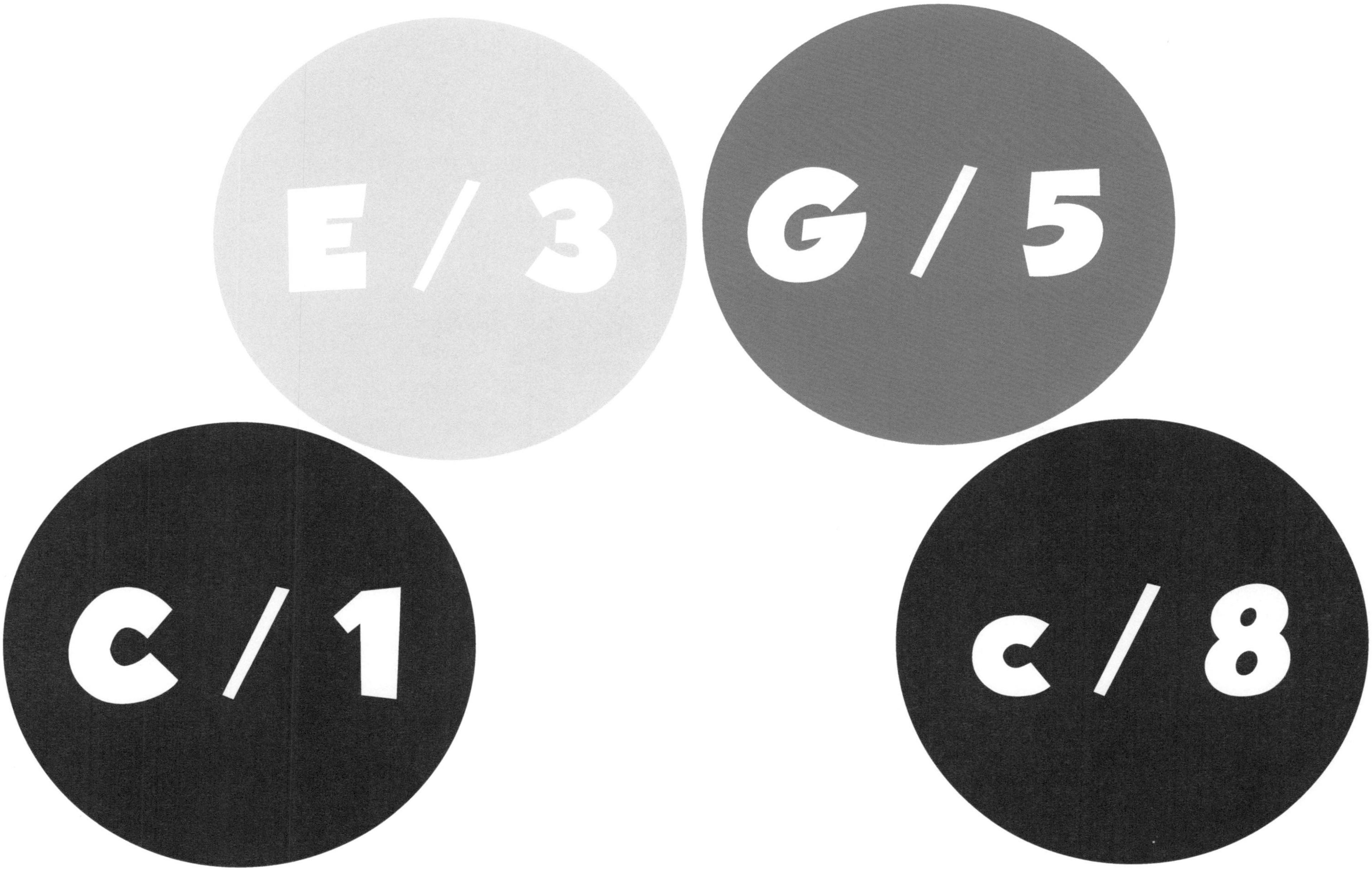

C
D
E
F
G
A
B
C

C
D
E
F
G
A
B
C

C Chord Slide

Lesson 2.5

☆☆☆☆☆

Play this song very SLOWLY as you carefully listen to the many different ways of playing the C Major Chord.

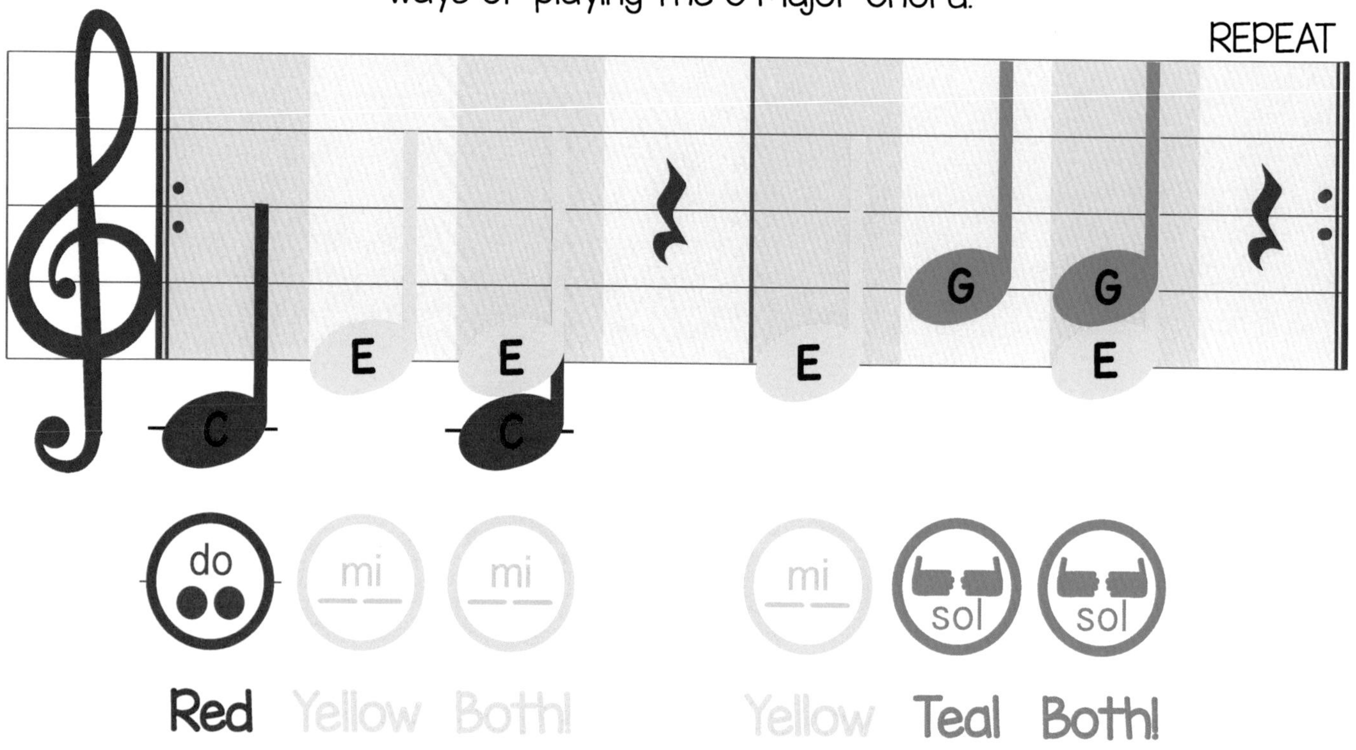

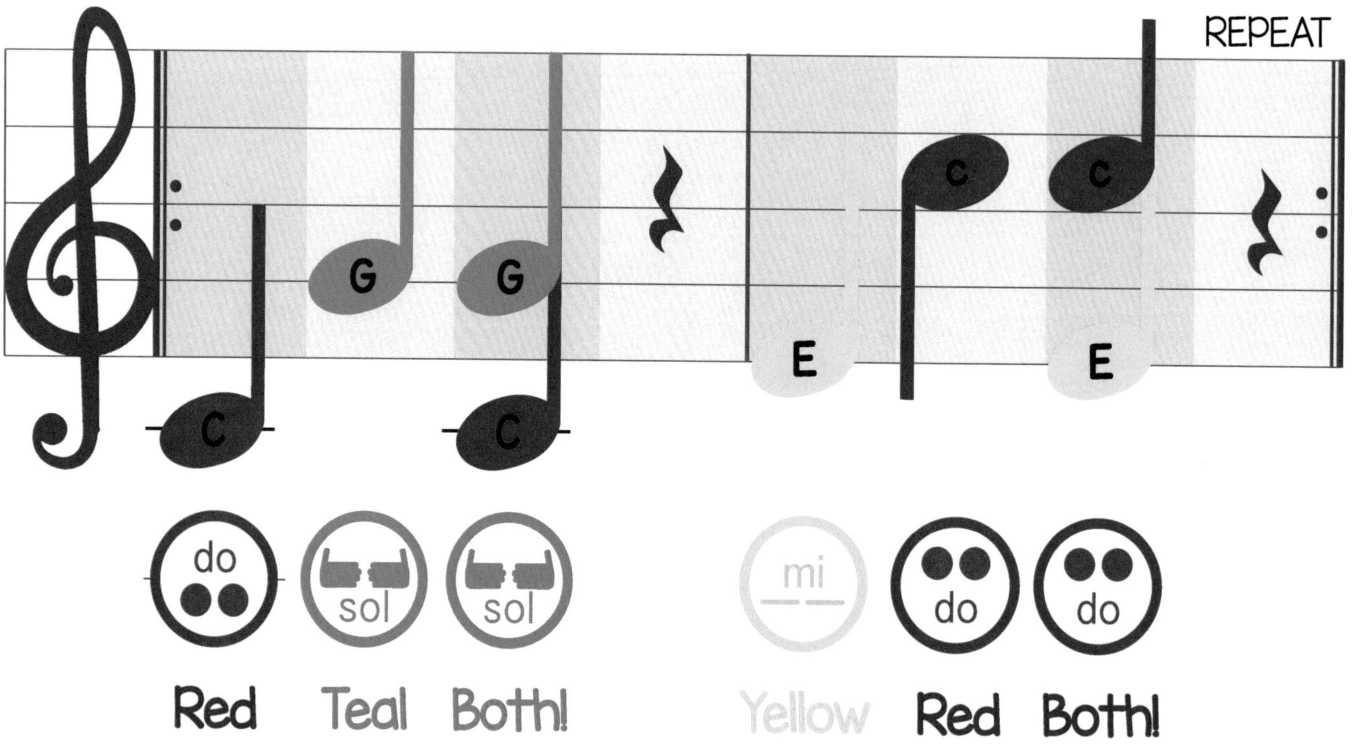

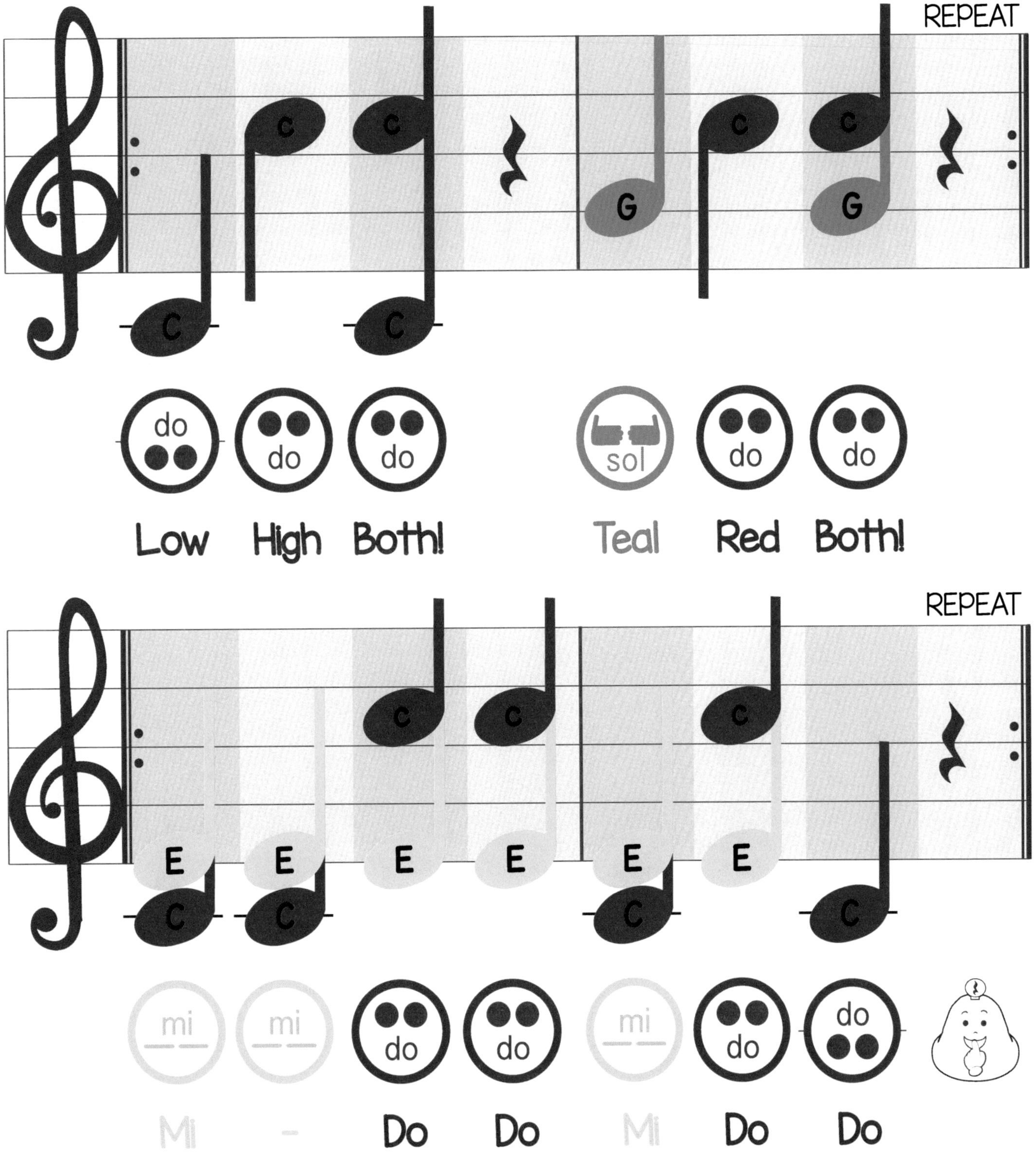
REPEAT
C
C
C
C
G
C
C
G
do
do
do
sol
do
do
Low
High
Both!
Teal
Red
Both!
REPEAT
C
C
C
E
E
E
E
E
E
C
C
C
C
mi
mi
do
do
mi
do
do
do
Mi
-
Do
Do
Mi
Do
Do

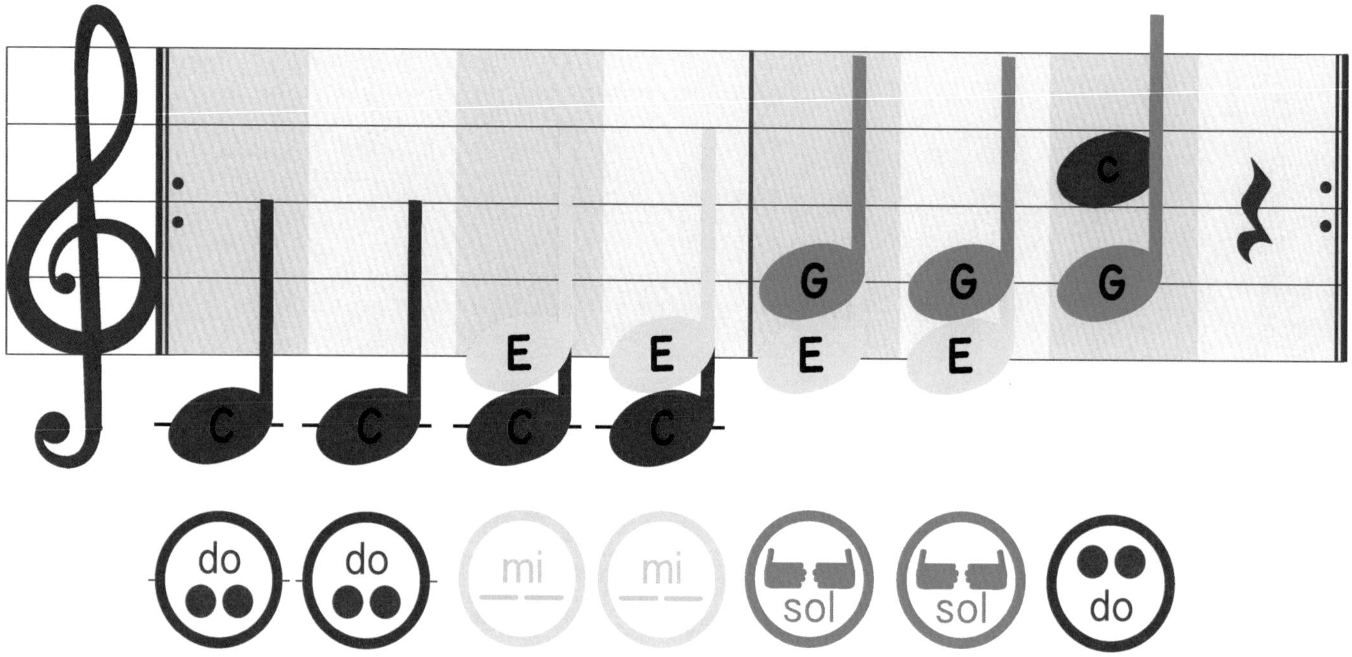

Do - Mi - Sol - Do

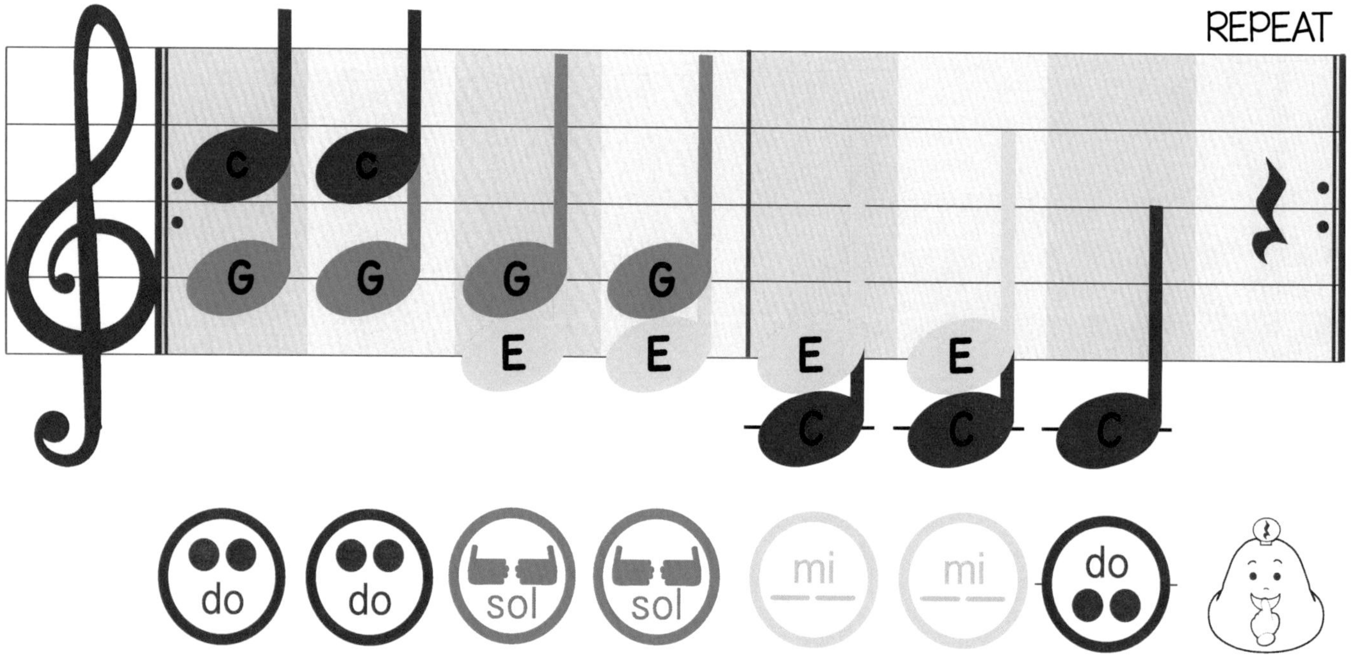

Do Do Sol Sol Mi Mi

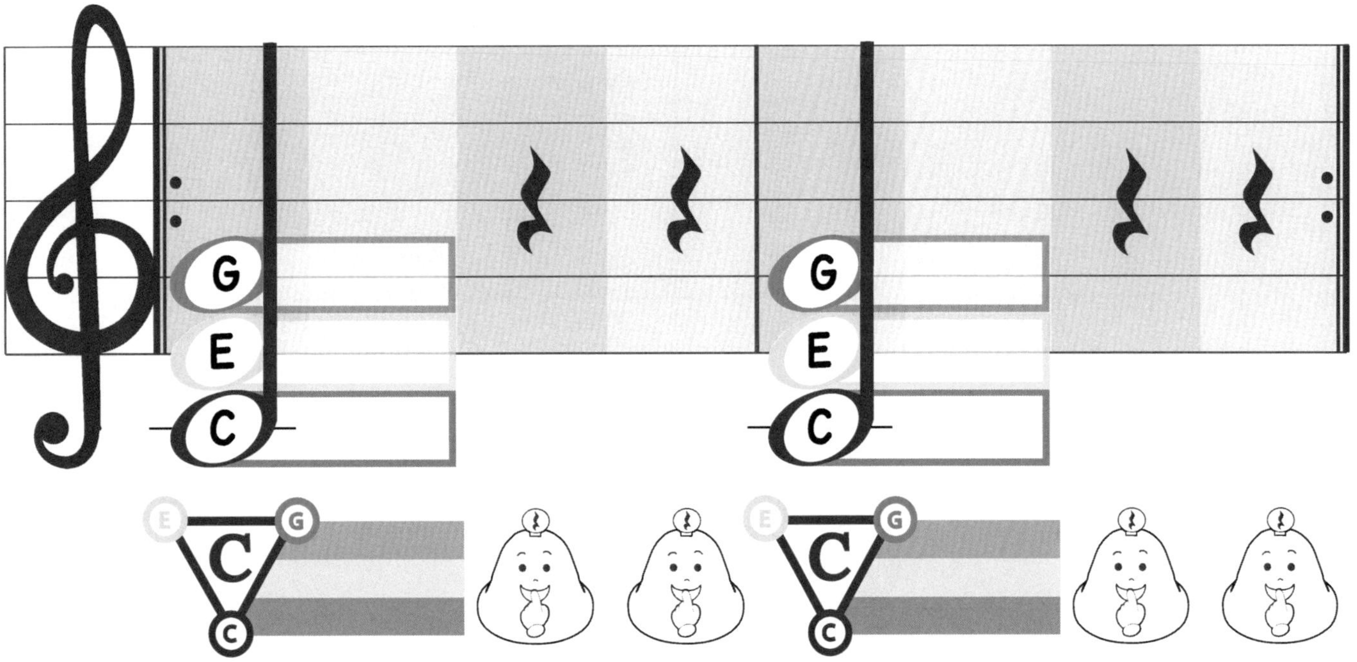
G
E
C
G
E
C
E
G
C
C
E
G
C
C

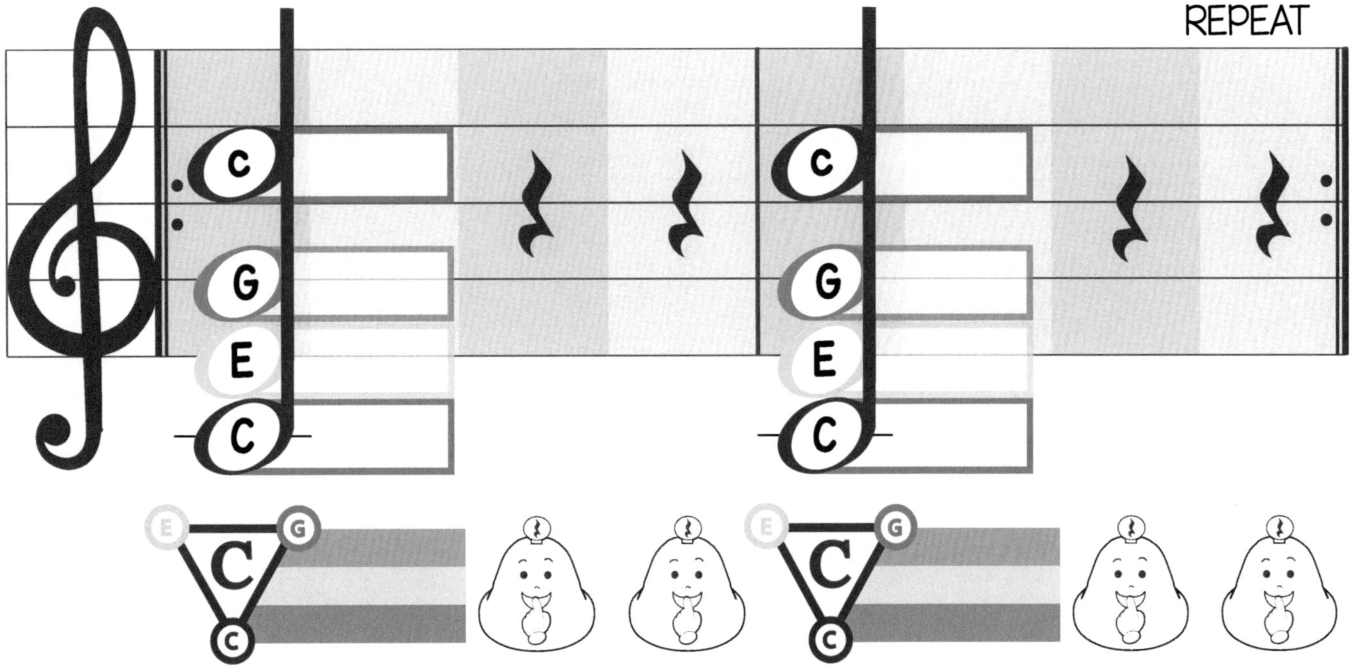
REPEAT
C
G
E
C
C
G
E
C
E
G
C
C
E
G
C
C

C Chord Boxes

Circle the bells in the boxes that make up a C chord and draw an X through the boxes that don't.

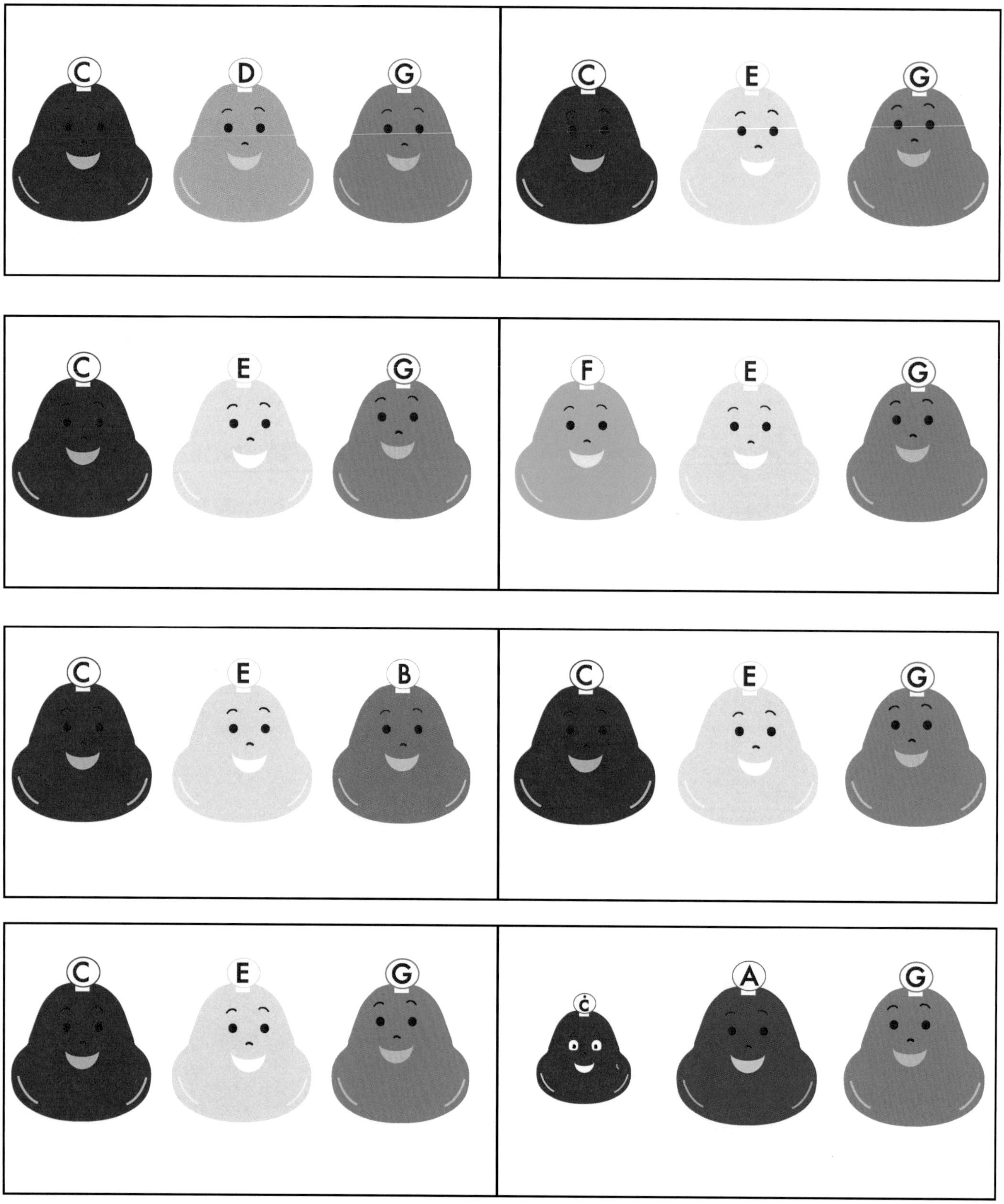

Make a C Chord

Draw a line to the bell in each group that matches each corner of the C chord triangle.

C Chord Trees

Circle the trees that make a C Chord. It's okay if the notes are out of order - they can still make a C chord! Then draw an X through the trees that are not C Chords.

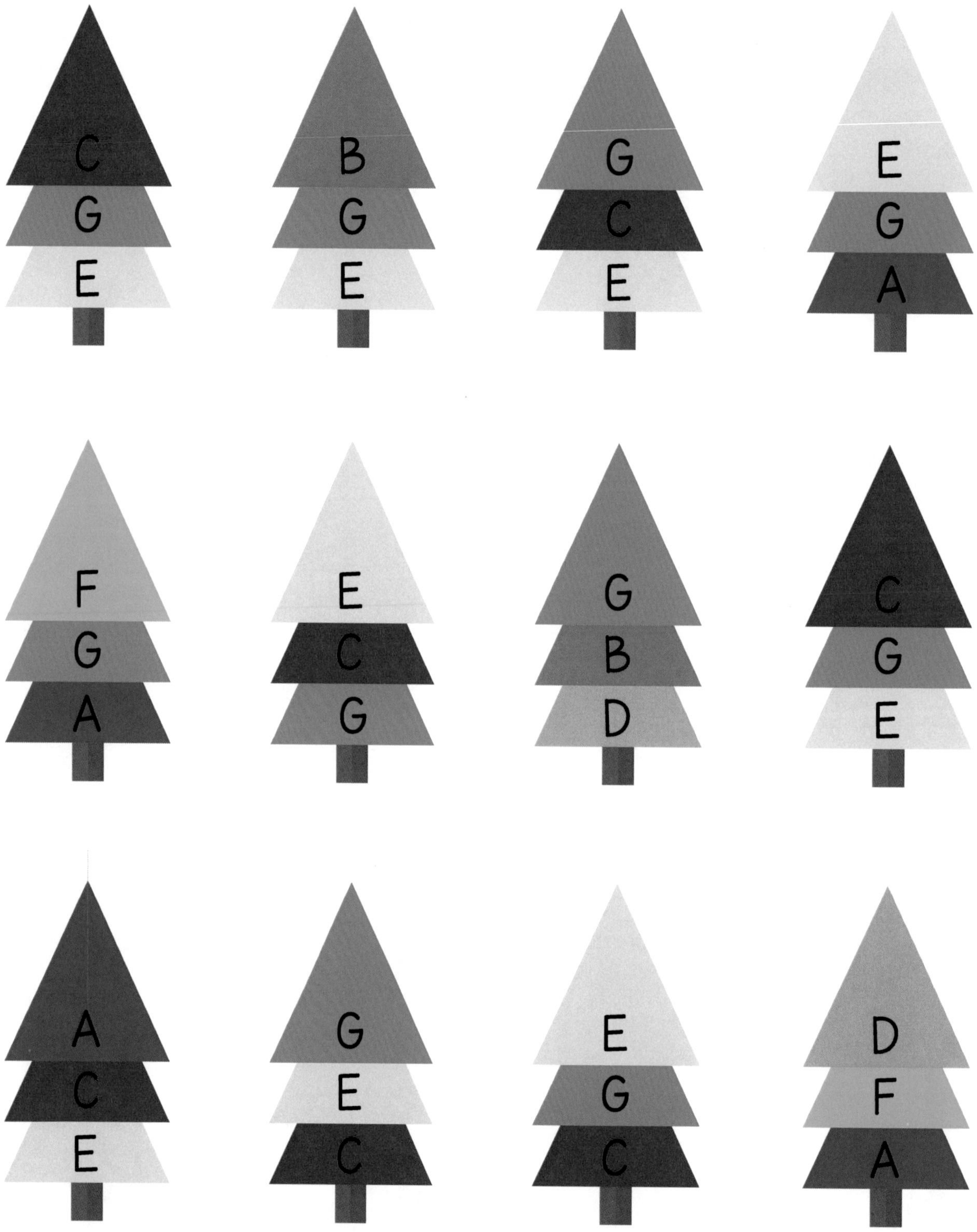

E Cube

Cut along the dotted line.
Fold the inside black lines.
Then tape your cube along the edges.
Practice vocabulary with your new cube and save it for an activity later this chapter!

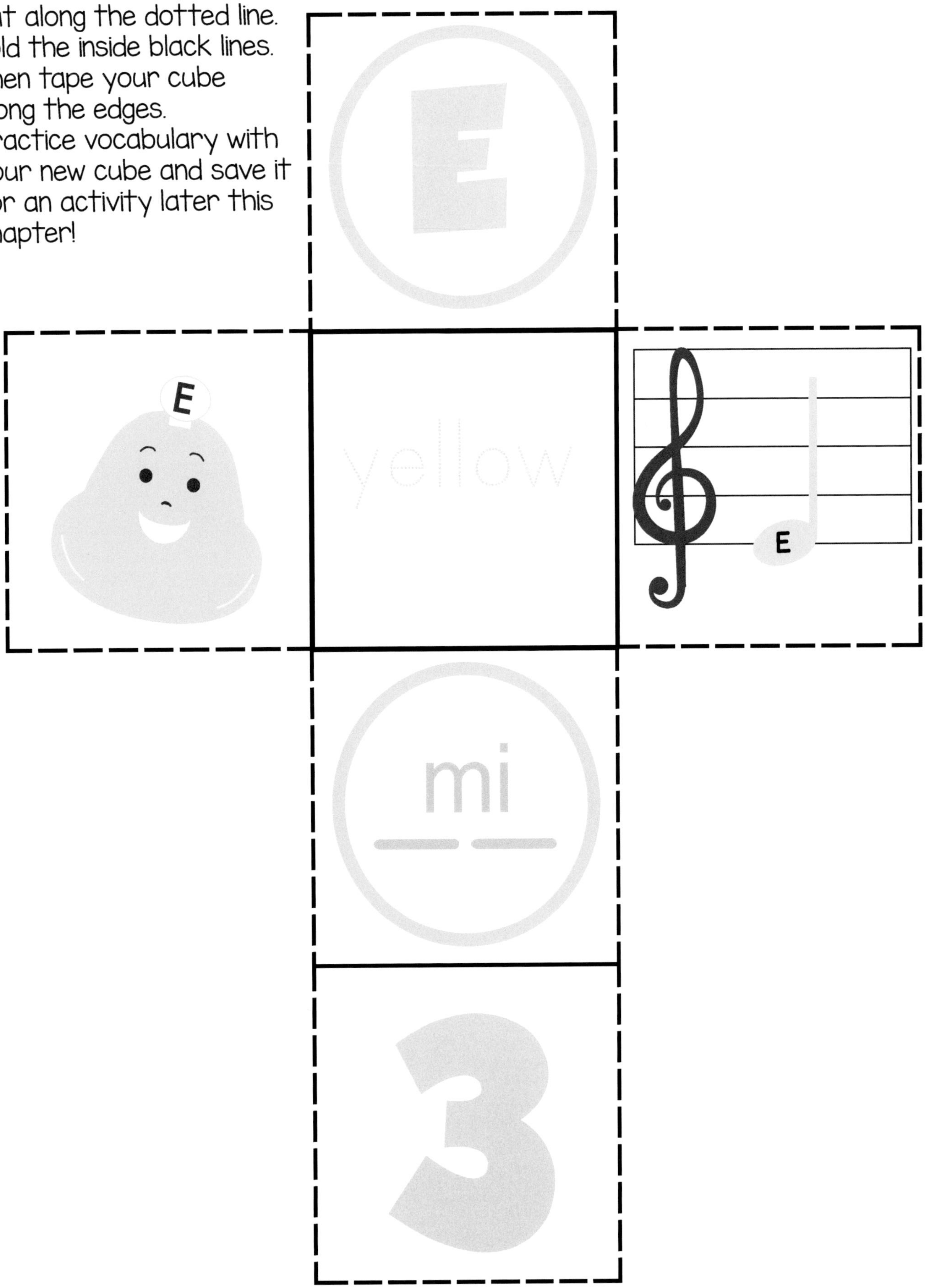

C
D
E
F
G
A
B
C

Chapter 2 Section 6: Pipes in C Major Lesson Guide

Objective

By the end of this section, students should recognize that each bell has its own color, letter, number, Solfège name and place on the staff.

Overview

This section introduces the C Major Scale in a typical up and down the scale kind of pattern. We practice singing with the colors, letters, numbers & Solfège names of all 8 of the bells.

Essential Question

How can a student describe the notes of the C Major Scale?

Instruction Tips

For this section, have students rip out the bell mat in their workbooks and use it as a mat for each of the songs and activities. As they color it, play this week's video in the background.

Materials

- Full set of bells
- Full set of crayons
- C Major Scale Video Access
- Workbook pages: 61-75
- Scissors
- Tape or Glue

Table of Contents

Complementary Activities

Use the G chord cube to play a vocabulary game. Toss the cube and catch it. Which ever panel your right thumb lands on, your learner has to tell you how that element represents G.

Section 2.6 Video Annotations

0:35 Pause here and make sure each student has his or her bells set up correctly.

1:36 Students sing along with the note names.

2:05 Students sing along with the Solfège names.

2:38 Students sing along with the numbers

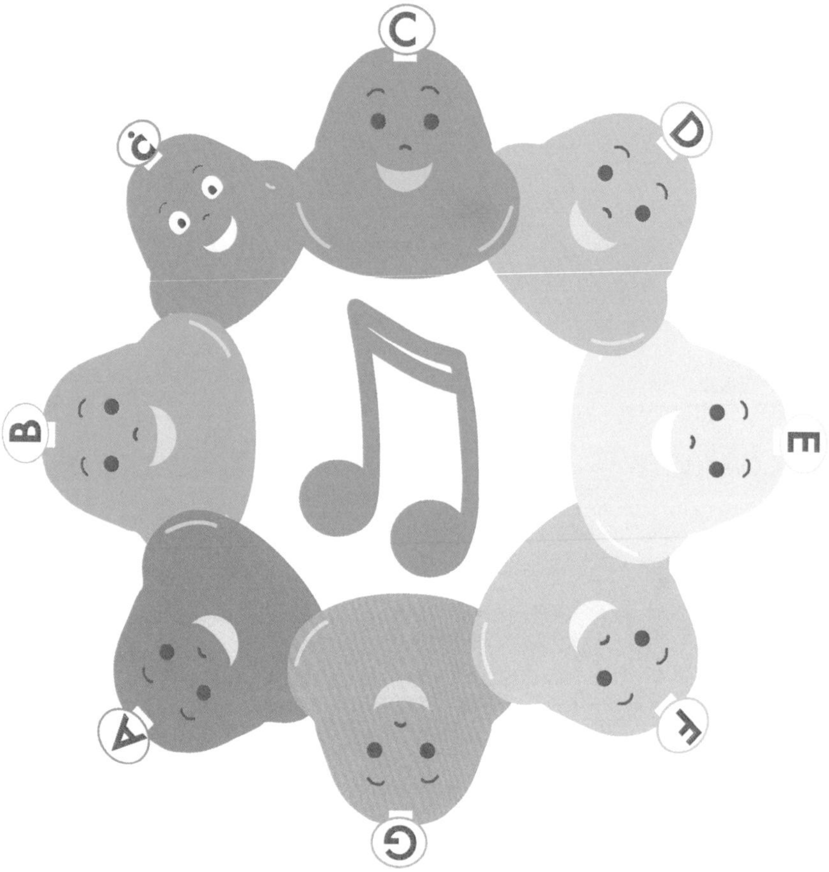
C
D
E
F
G
A
B
C

C Major Bell Mat

Use this bell mat for any song that uses all 8 bells!

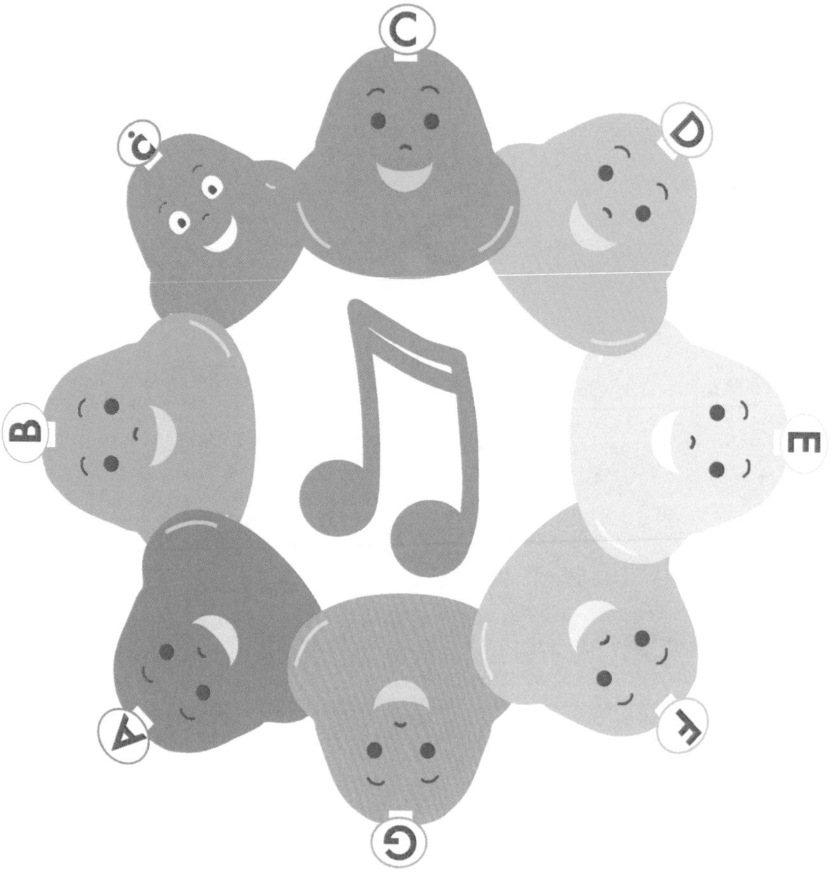
C
D
E
F
G
A
B
C

G / 5
Teal
A / 6
Purple
B / 7
Pink
C / 8
Red
Sol
La
Ti
do

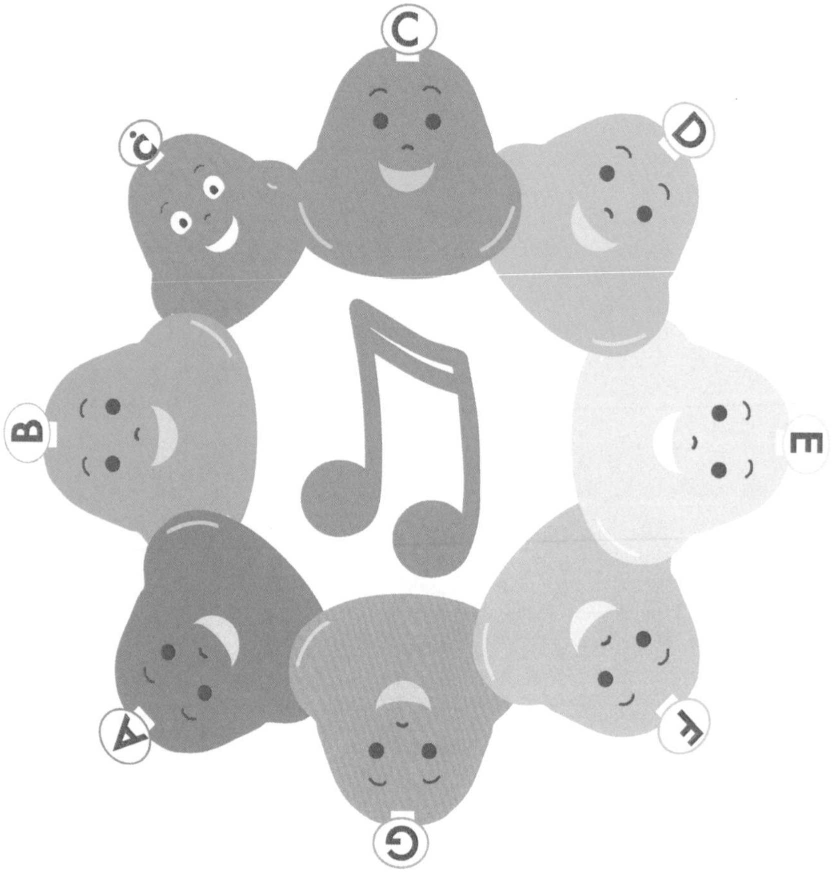
C
D
E
F
G
A
B
C

C
D
E
F
G
A
B
C

C Major Scale

Lesson 2.6

☆☆☆☆☆

As you play this song, make sure you repeat the song with each different verse. Try to get comfortable singing with the letter names, the colors and the Solfège syllables while playing your instrument. And for extra perfect timing, don't forget to use a metronome!

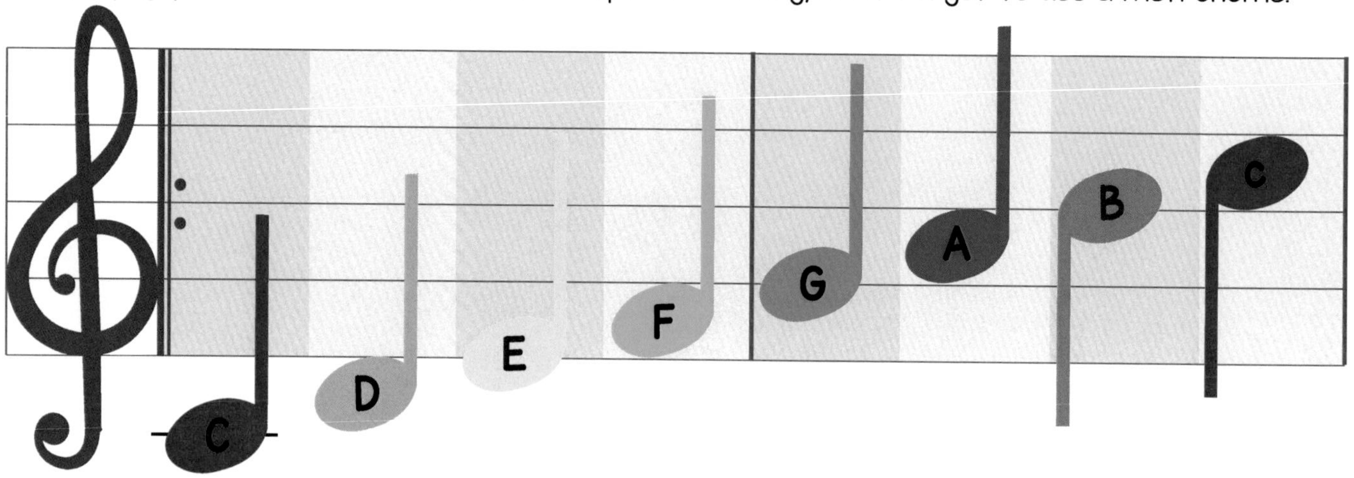

1st Time Sing	Red	Orange	Yellow	Green	Teal	Purple	Pink	red
2nd Time Sing	do	re	mi	fa	sol	la	ti	do

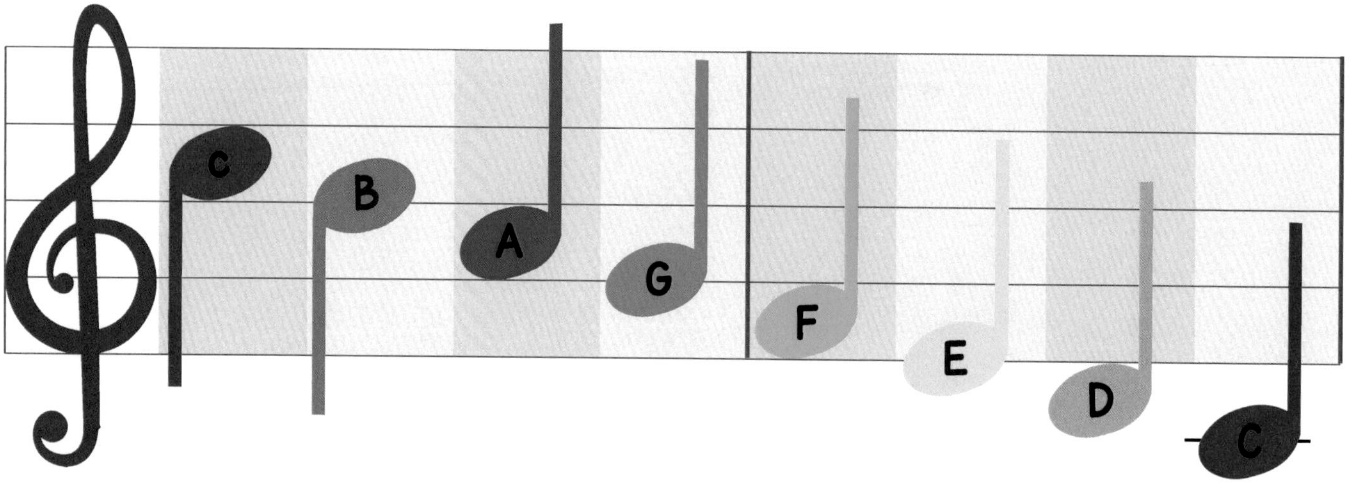

1st Time Sing	red	Pink	Purple	Teal	Green	Yellow	Orange	Red
2nd Time Sing	do	ti	la	sol	fa	mi	re	do

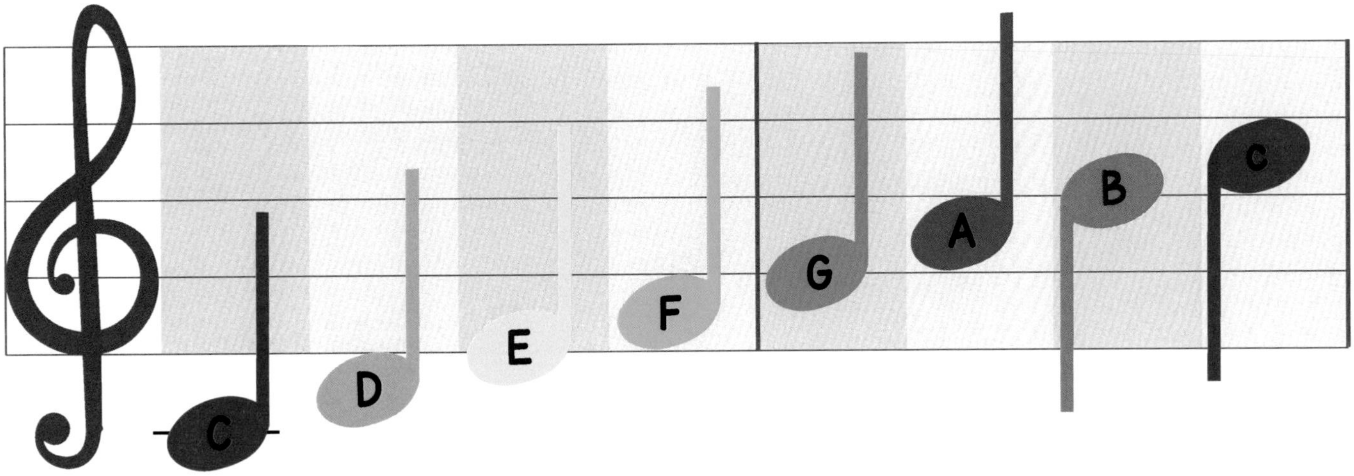

1st Time Sing	C	D	E	F	G	A	B	c
2nd Time Sing	1	2	3	4	5	6	7	8

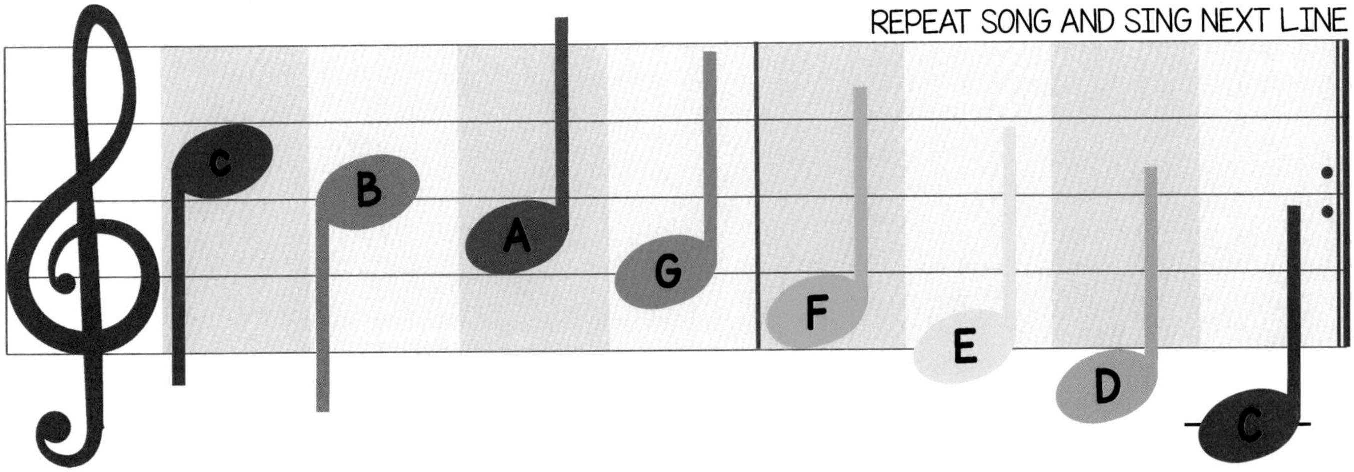

1st Time Sing	c	B	A	G	F	E	D	C
2nd Time Sing	8	7	6	5	4	3	2	1

Bells by Number

Draw a line between each bell its scale degree name.

1

2

3

4

5

6

7

8

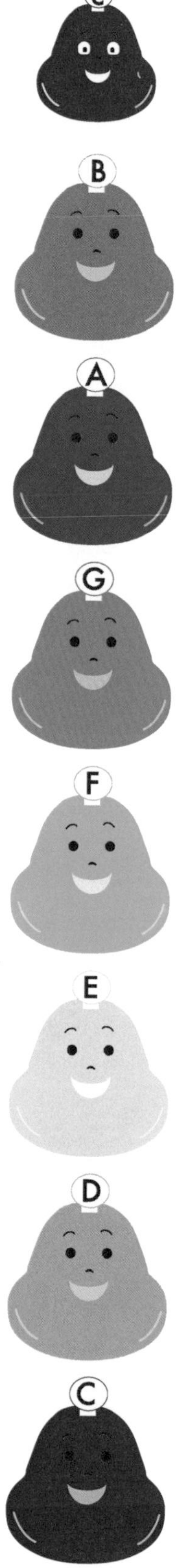

Bells by Solfège

Draw a line between each bell its Solfège name.

Do

Mi

Fa

do

Ti

La

Sol

Re

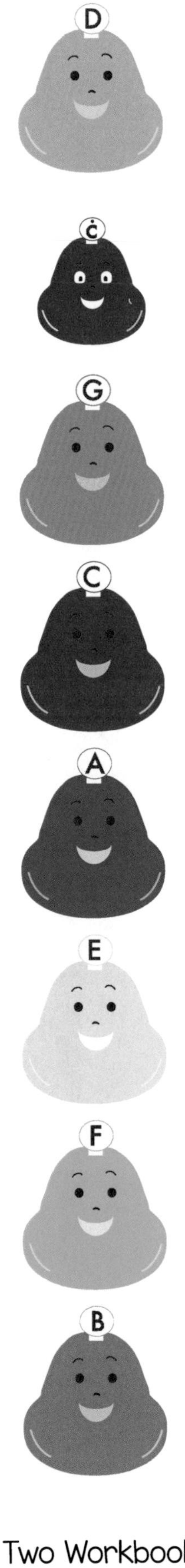

Piano Rainbow

Use the numbers on the piano to color a rainbow!

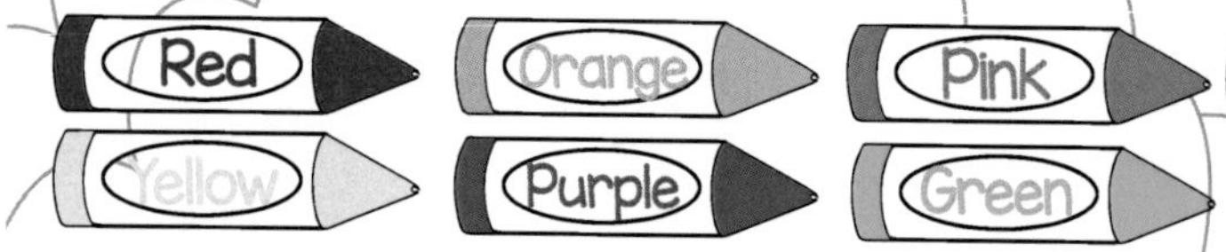

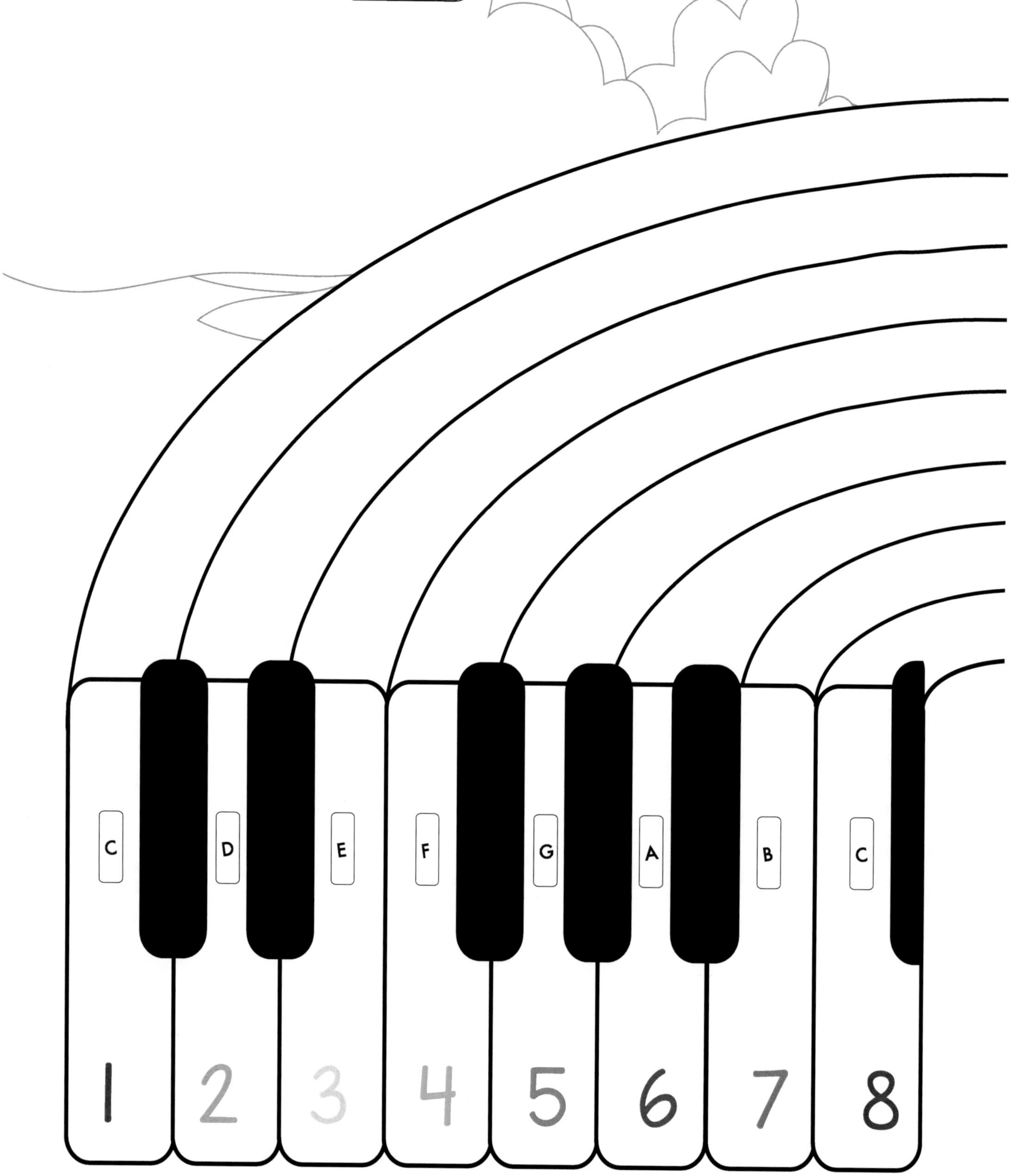

C
D
E
F
G
A
B
C

G Cube

Cut along the dotted line.
Fold the inside black lines.
Then tape your cube along the edges.
Practice vocabulary with your new cube and save it for an activity later this chapter!

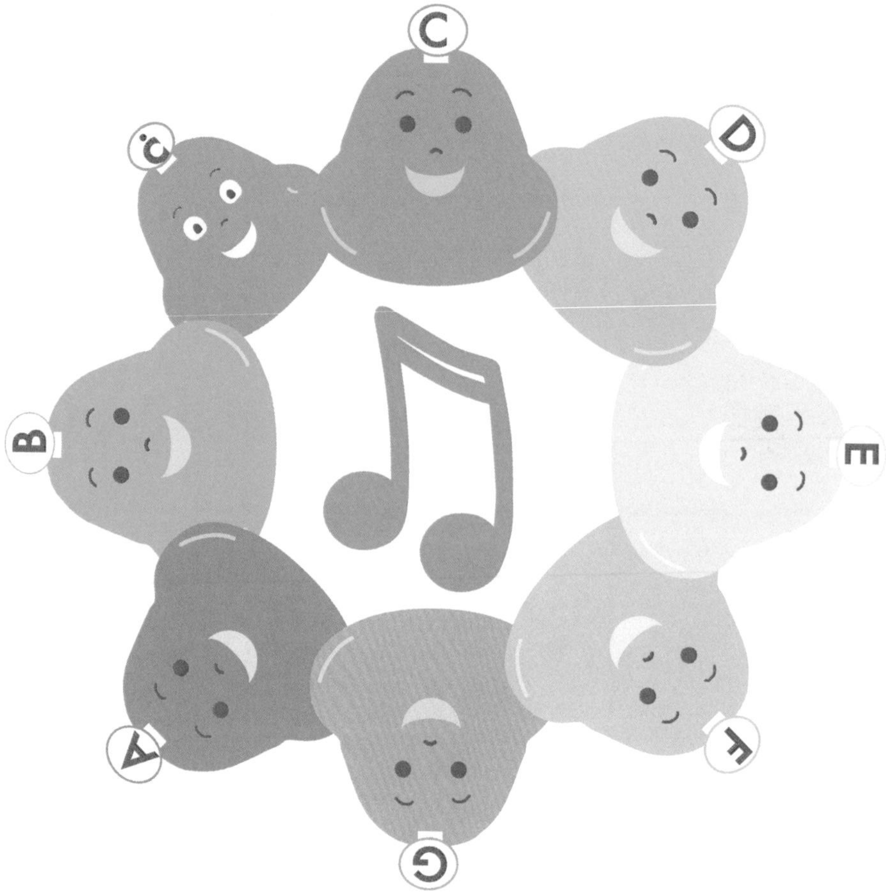
C
D
E
F
G
A
B
C

Cube Stacking

Use the cubes you made to stack the following arrangements. After you stack each one, play the chords you made.

Objective

By the end of this section, students should be able to differentiate between high and low C.

Overview

This section is a listening game. Students will guess between high and low C.

Essential Question

How can a student differentiate between high and low C?

Instruction Tips

If your students want to play this listening game several times, instead of having them fill out the worksheet, tell them to hold up their lion and bird cards from earlier in the chapter.

Materials

- Red Crayon
- What Note Is It? Video Access
- Workbook pages: 77

Table of Contents

Complementary Activities

Make up your own listening game with high and low C. You could even add in a call and response element by adding patterns.

Section 2.L Video Annotations

0:28 Pause and make sure that each student has high c and low C out. Give them time to play each bell and say its note name.

0:40 Pause and let your learner guess the first note name before Rex reveals it!

1:06 Pause and let your learner guess the second note name before Rex reveals it!

1:32 Pause and let your learner guess the third note name before Rex reveals it! Explain to students that this will be the last time you pause before moving on. Be sure that your learner is circling his or her guesses on the What Note Is It workbook page.

Red

What Note Is It?

Draw a circle around the bell you hear in each box!

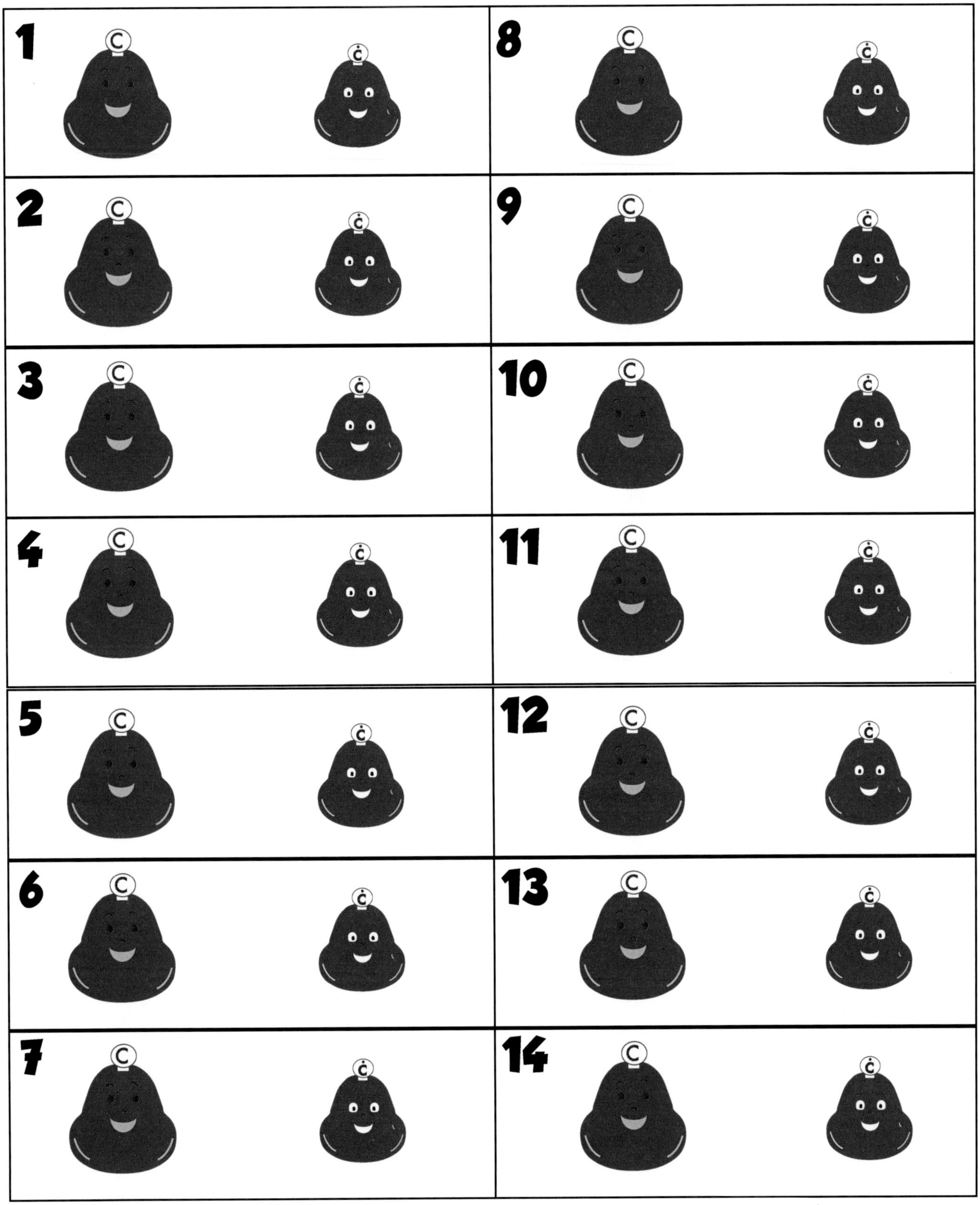

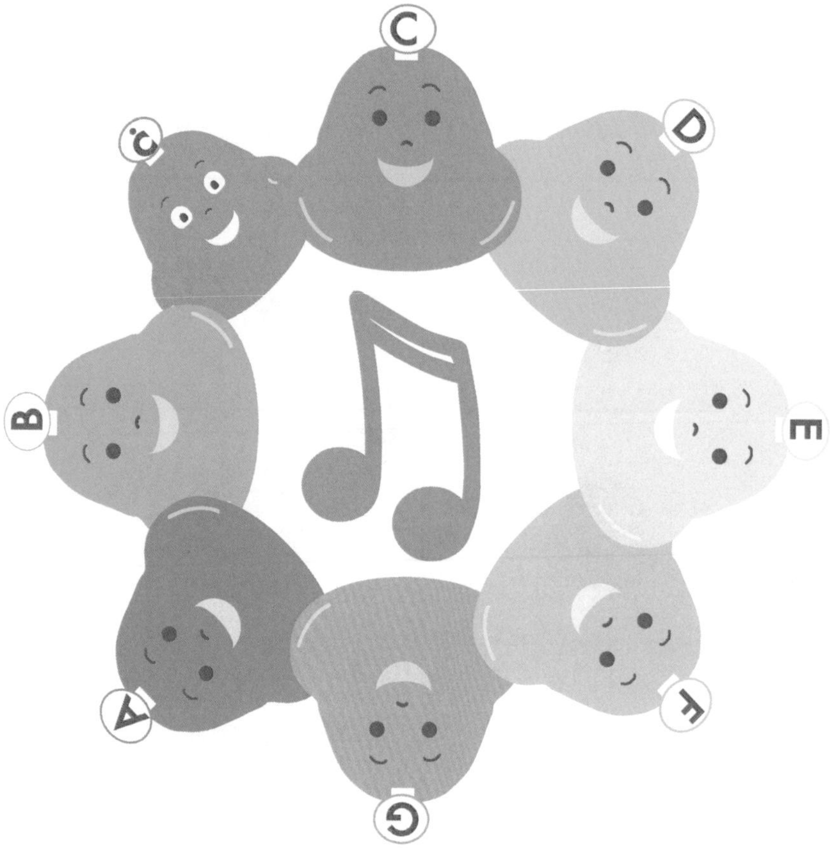
C
D
E
F
G
A
B
C

Prodigies Playground

CONGRATULATIONS

You've Completed

Preschool Prodigies

CHAPTER 2

Nice work!

------------------------ Teacher Signature

------------------------ Date

52677761R00046

Made in the USA
Columbia, SC
06 March 2019